IMPACT
CALIFORNIA
SOCIAL STUDIES

INQUIRY JOURNAL

PRINCIPLES OF
ECONOMICS

Mc
Graw
Hill

Cover Photo Credits: (l to r, t to b) Shutterstock/Orientaly; gilaxia/E+/Getty Images; Shutterstock/isak55; heyengel/iStock/Getty Images Plus; United States Mint image

mheducation.com/prek-12

Send all inquiries to:
McGraw-Hill Education
8787 Orion Place
Columbus, OH 43240

ISBN: 978-0-07-693883-4
MHID: 0-07-693883-2

Printed in the United States of America.

4 5 6 7 8 9 10 11 LWI 24 23 22 21 20

Table of Contents

UNIT 7
THE GLOBAL ECONOMY

CHAPTER 19
Personal Financial Literacy

ESSENTIAL QUESTIONS

How can financial institutions help you increase and better manage your money?
What are the different types of business organizations?
How can you take control of your own money?

Dear Student,

Many of us are curious, and we have questions about many things. We have the more personal questions, such as, "What type of job or career might I be suited for?" or "How do I learn the best way to save money to buy the things I want or need?" We also have questions of a larger nature about the world around us. These might include questions such as the following: "What does being treated like an adult mean?" "How do I understand what I see or read about in school, online, or in the news?" "Why do nations go to war with one another?" "Why do political parties clash with one another so frequently?"

Asking good questions helps us take charge of our own learning. Learning to ask good questions is a process, as "yes" or "no" types of questions do not get us very far in discovering why events happened or why people feel as they do. Once we master this process, however, we become better thinkers and researchers and can find out more about subjects that interest us. Asking good questions is also important if we want to understand and affect the world around us.

In this book, as in other parts of the program, there will be Essential Questions that you will research. These are universal questions. Examples of such questions include the following: "In what ways do people cope with the problem of scarcity?" "What factors affect prices?" "How do we determine the economic and social well-being of the United States?" "What is the role of savings in the financial system?" You will develop some of your own Supporting Questions to help you answer the Essential Questions.

As you move through the study of economics, you will be reading primary and secondary sources about a specific time period. **Primary sources**—whether they are diaries, poetry, letters, or artwork—were created by people who saw or experienced the event they are describing. **Secondary sources**—whether they are biographies, or history books, or your student text, are created after an event, by people who were not part of the original event.

Once you have completed the readings and answered the accompanying questions, there is a "Report Your Findings" project in which you answer the Essential Questions. You will work on some parts of the project by yourself, and you will work on other parts of the project with your classmates. You will be given many opportunities to take informed action. This means that you will use what you have learned and apply it to a current issue in a way that interests you. You will share this information with other students or with people in your community.

Thinking Like an Economist

In this unit, you will learn what economics is and how economics affects your everyday life. You will also study economic systems around the world and compare them to the American free enterprise system. Read the Essential Questions for each of the three chapters in this unit and think about how they will help you understand the subject of economics.

TALK ABOUT IT

Select one Essential Question from each chapter in this unit and discuss it with a partner. What type of information would you need to know in order to answer it? For example, to understand the American free enterprise system, you must be familiar with the basic elements of capitalism.

DIRECTIONS: Write down two Supporting Questions for each chapter that will help you understand one or more of the Essential Questions in the chapter.

Chapter 1 What is Economics?
ESSENTIAL QUESTION

- *In what ways do people cope with the problem of scarcity?*

MY RESEARCH QUESTIONS

Supporting Question 1:

_____

_____

Supporting Question 2:

_____

_____

Chapter 2 Economic Systems and Decision Making
ESSENTIAL QUESTION

- *How does an economic system help a society deal with the fundamental problem of scarcity?*

MY RESEARCH QUESTIONS

Supporting Question 1:

_____

_____

Supporting Question 2:

_____

_____

Chapter 3 The American Free Enterprise System
ESSENTIAL QUESTIONS

- *What are the benefits of a free enterprise economy?*

- *What are the major economic and social goals of the American free enterprise system?*

MY RESEARCH QUESTIONS

Supporting Question 1:

_____

_____

Supporting Question 2:

_____

_____

INDEPENDENT INQUIRY ACTIVITIES
Chapters 2 and 3

For Chapters 2 and 3, your teacher may ask you to conduct a research project using the Research Questions you have developed above. For these independent inquiry projects, you will follow these steps.

1. Research the answers to your Supporting Questions using online and library resources in addition to the Student Edition text. Analyze the primary and secondary sources you have located and take notes.
2. Select a method to report your findings, such as a research paper, an oral presentation, or a visual essay. Prepare your findings and submit them to your teacher or share them with your class.
3. To conclude, think of ways you could take action based on your findings. Choose one way to get involved.

GUIDED INQUIRY ACTIVITY
Chapter 1

This unit's guided inquiry activity focuses on Chapter 1 *What is Economics?* In the guided inquiry activity, you will follow the same process as the independent activities; however, primary sources and questions about these sources and the Student Edition text are provided to help guide you through the inquiry process.

Reread the Supporting Questions you developed for Chapter 1 as you prepare to search for evidence in the Student Edition text.

Scarcity and the Science of Economics

DIRECTIONS: Search for evidence in Chapter 1, Lesson 1, to help you answer the following questions.

1 **SUMMARIZING** Why does every society face the problem of scarcity?

_____

_____

_____

2 **ANALYZING IDEAS** An electronics store sells new computers. Are computers durable goods or nondurable goods? Are computers consumer goods or capital goods? Why?

_____

_____

_____

_____

_____

3 **ANALYZING CENTRAL IDEAS** Why are diamonds more expensive than water even though we need water to survive?

_____

_____

_____

_____

4 **INFERRING** A local restaurant is offering a special deal. Customers who order one large pizza get a second large pizza for free. Is the second pizza really free? Why or why not?

_____

_____

_____

_____

ESSENTIAL QUESTION

In what ways do people cope with the problem of scarcity?

As you gather evidence to answer the Essential Question, think about:

- why scarcity exists in every society.
- how societies decide WHAT, HOW, and FOR WHOM to produce.
- how economists study scarcity and its effects.

My Notes

_____

_____

_____

_____

_____

_____

5 **DETERMINING CENTRAL IDEAS** What are the three questions all societies face?

_____

_____

_____

_____

6 **INTEGRATING INFORMATION** The four elements of study in the field of economics are description, analysis, explanation, and prediction. The items below are examples of each element. Write the correct element next to the corresponding example.

An economist wonders why a new tax law might affect GDP.	
An economist thinks that people are spending more money now because they believe a new tax law will decrease their incomes in the future.	
An economist notices that GDP has increased in the weeks leading up to the passage of a new tax law.	
An economist says that GDP will probably return to normal levels after the tax law is passed.	

ESSENTIAL QUESTION

In what ways do people cope with the problem of scarcity?

An Inquiry Into the Nature and Causes of the Wealth of Nations

DIRECTIONS: Read the excerpt from *An Inquiry Into the Nature and Causes of the Wealth of Nations* by Adam Smith. Then answer the questions that follow.

EXPLORE THE CONTEXT: Adam Smith's book *An Inquiry Into the Nature and Causes of the Wealth of Nations* (often referred to more simply as *The Wealth of Nations*) represents one of the earliest contributions to the field of economics. Prior to the publication of *The Wealth of Nations* in 1776, most countries used the value of their silver and gold deposits as a measure of their nation's wealth. Smith, however, challenged this theory and suggested that wealth should instead be determined by how much a country could produce. This excerpt comes from the introduction to *The Wealth of Nations.* In the excerpt, Smith examines the relationship between a nation's labor and its wealth.

Copyright © McGraw-Hill Education; TEXT: Smith, Adam. 1814. An Inquiry into the Nature and Causes of the Wealth of Nations. Edited by David Buchanan. Vol. 1. Edinburgh: Oliphant, Waugh & Innes.

PRIMARY SOURCE: BOOK

66 The annual labour of every nation is the fund which originally supplies it with all the necessaries and conveniencies of life . . . which consist always either in the immediate produce of that labour, or in what is purchased with that produce from other nations.

According, therefore, as this produce, or what is purchased with it, bears a greater or smaller proportion to the number of those who are to consume it, the nation will be better or worse supplied with all the necessaries and conveniencies for which it has occasion.

But this proportion must in every nation be regulated by two different circumstances: first, by the skill, dexterity, and judgment with which its labour is generally applied; and, secondly, by the proportion between the number of those who are employed in useful labour, and that of those who are not so employed. Whatever be the soil, climate, or extent of territory of any particular nation, the abundance or scantiness of its annual supply must, in that particular situation, depend upon those two circumstances. 99

—Adam Smith, *An Inquiry Into the Nature and Causes of the Wealth of Nations,* 1776

VOCABULARY

necessaries: necessities

conveniencies: an old-fashioned spelling of the modern word *conveniences*; something that makes life easier or more comfortable

produce: a product that fulfills needs and wants

dexterity: ability to perform tasks, especially those related to the hands or physical movements

scantiness: lack; insufficiency

1 **UNDERSTANDING CONTEXT** Given the time period in which Smith wrote and published *The Wealth of Nations,* what items might Smith have considered to be "conveniencies of life"? If a writer used this same phrase today, to what might he or she be referring?

_____

_____

_____

2 **ANALYZING CENTRAL IDEAS** According to Smith, under what circumstances would a nation have "all the necessaries and conveniencies for which it has occasion"?

_____

_____

3 **DETERMINING MEANING** According to Smith, what is "the fund" that provides for the nation's needs?

_____

_____

4 **CITING TEXT EVIDENCE** At the time that *The Wealth of Nations* was published, many nations did not believe that it was beneficial to trade with other nations. Would Smith agree with this sentiment? How do you know? Use text evidence to support your answer.

_____

_____

_____

5 **INFERRING** Which country would Smith expect to produce more than it consumes: one with many young children or one with a large adult population? Why?

_____

_____

_____

6 **EVALUATING** Today's world is very different from the world in 1776. Among other changes, people live longer, they travel much farther from their birthplace, they use advanced technology every day, and they marry and have children later in life. Based on Smith's theories, how might these changes affect a nation's wealth?

_____

_____

_____

_____

Our Economic Choices

DIRECTIONS: Search for evidence in Chapter 1, Lesson 2, to help you answer the following questions.

1A **DETERMINING CENTRAL IDEAS** What are the four factors of production?

_____

_____

1B **ANALYZING IDEAS** How would all four factors of production be used to produce a cup of coffee?

_____

_____

_____

_____

The production possibilities curve below shows all the combinations of clothing and cars that can be produced by the country Alpha. Use the production possibilities curve to answer questions 2A, 2B, and 2C.

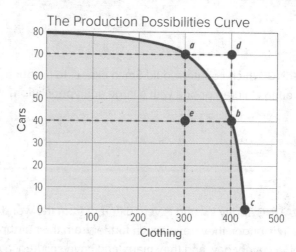

The Production Possibilities Curve

2A **INTERPRETING CHARTS/GRAPHS** If Alpha produces 60 cars, how many units of clothing can Alpha produce?

_____

_____

ESSENTIAL QUESTION

In what ways do people cope with the problem of scarcity?

As you gather evidence to answer the Essential Question, think about:

- how the four factors of production are used to create a product.
- how a production possibilities curve represents various combinations of goods and services that can be produced.
- how trade-offs and opportunity costs are similar and different.
- the rights and responsibilities of consumers.

My Notes

_____

_____

_____

_____

_____

_____

2B **INFERRING** What must happen in order for Alpha to increase production from point **b** to point **d**?

_____

_____

2C **INTEGRATING INFORMATION** If Alpha is initially producing 40 cars and 400 units of clothing (point **b**), what is the opportunity cost of producing 425 units of clothing instead of 400?

_____

3A **MAKING DECISIONS** You have just graduated from high school, and you received a graduation gift of $1,000. Fill in the decision-making grid below to decide how you will spend the money.

DECISION-MAKING GRID

Criteria / Alternatives	Will allow my money to grow	Mom and Dad will approve	Will make the summer before college more fun	Will make my life easier when I get to campus in the fall
Put the money in a savings account				
Take a trip to Europe with friends				
Buy a used car				
Buy books for college				

3B **ANALYZING ISSUES** Based on how you filled in the decision-making grid, what decision did you make? Why?

_____

_____

ESSENTIAL QUESTION

In what ways do people cope with the problem of scarcity?

VOCABULARY

frauds: scams; deceptions

succeeding: next; later

standard of living: quality of life based on ownership of necessities and luxuries that make life easier

inferior: lower quality; less good

exorbitant: excessive; too high

Special Message to the Congress on Protecting the Consumer Interest

DIRECTIONS: Read the speech and answer the questions that follow.

EXPLORE THE CONTEXT: In March 1962, President John F. Kennedy spoke to Congress about the need for consumer protections. His speech resulted in the Consumer Bill of Rights. Initially, there were four consumer rights, but additional rights have been added since then.

PRIMARY SOURCE: SPEECH

"Consumers, by definition, include us all. They are the largest economic group in the economy, affecting and affected by almost every public and private economic decision. Two-thirds of all spending in the economy is by consumers. But they are the only important group in the economy who are not effectively organized, whose views are often not heard.

The federal Government—by nature the highest spokesman for all the people—has a special obligation to be alert to the consumer's needs and to advance the consumer's interests. Ever since legislation was enacted in 1872 to protect the consumer from frauds involving use of the U.S. mail, the Congress and Executive Branch have been increasingly aware of their responsibility to make certain that our Nation's economy fairly and adequately serves consumers' interests.

In the main, it has served them extremely well. Each succeeding generation has enjoyed both higher income and a greater variety of goods and services. As a result our standard of living is the highest in the world—and, in less than 20 years, it should rise an additional 50 percent.

Fortunate as we are, we nevertheless cannot afford waste in consumption any more than we can afford inefficiency in business or Government. If consumers are offered inferior products, if prices are exorbitant, if drugs are unsafe or worthless, if the consumer is unable to choose on an informed basis, then his dollar is wasted, his health and safety may be threatened, and the national interest suffers. On the other hand, increased efforts to make the best possible use of their incomes can contribute more to the well-being of most families than equivalent efforts to raise their incomes."

—John F. Kennedy, "Special Message to the Congress on Protecting the Consumer Interest," March 15, 1962

1 **DETERMINING CENTRAL IDEAS** What is the main idea of Kennedy's speech?

_____

_____

2 **INFERRING** Kennedy says that "two-thirds of all spending in the economy is by consumers." Who might be responsible for the last third of spending?

_____

_____

3 **CITING TEXT EVIDENCE** According to Kennedy, what happens when consumers are not protected? Cite text evidence to support your answer.

_____

_____

4A **ANALYZING IDEAS** Kennedy says that "increased efforts to make the best possible use of [consumers'] incomes can contribute more to the well-being of most families than equivalent efforts to raise their incomes." What does Kennedy mean by this?

_____

_____

_____

_____

4B **EVALUATING POINT OF VIEW** Based on your answer to question 4A, do you agree with Kennedy? Why or why not?

_____

_____

_____

5 CIVICS The consumer experience has changed immensely since 1962. For example, people today frequently shop online, and producers have many new methods of advertising their products. What new consumer protection laws might be necessary today that were not necessary in 1962?

_____

_____

_____

Using Economic Models

DIRECTIONS: Search for evidence in Chapter 1, Lesson 3, to help you answer the following questions.

1 ANALYZING IDEAS Why do the division of labor and specialization increase productivity?

_____

_____

_____

Look at the diagram below showing the circular flow of economic activity. Use the diagram to answer questions 2A and 2B.

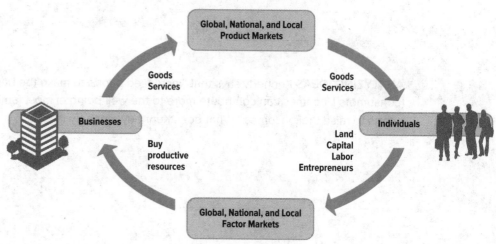

2A INTEGRATING INFORMATION In your own words, briefly summarize the interactions between product markets, factor markets, businesses, and individuals.

_____

_____

_____

_____

_____

ESSENTIAL QUESTION

In what ways do people cope with the problem of scarcity?

As you gather evidence to answer the Essential Question, think about:

- the factors that lead to economic growth.
- how the factor market and the product market contribute to the circular flow of economic activity.
- why economic models are used to explain economic activity.
- how a cost-benefit analysis can be used to make decisions.
- how studying economics can help people make better economic choices.

My Notes

_____

_____

_____

_____

_____

2B **ANALYZING IDEAS** Why is the diagram an example of an economic model?

_____

_____

_____

_____

3A **MAKING DECISIONS** You have just gotten a new job and are deciding whether to buy a new car or take public transportation to work each day. Complete the cost-benefit analysis to help you make your decision.

Cost-Benefit Analysis

Buying a car		Using public transportation	
Costs:	Benefits:	Costs:	Benefits:

3B **ANALYZING ISSUES** Based on your answer to question 3A, would you choose to buy a car or take public transportation? Why?

_____

_____

4 **SUMMARIZING** How will studying economics help you in the future?

_____

_____

ESSENTIAL QUESTION

In what ways do people cope with the problem of scarcity?

My Life and Work

DIRECTIONS: Read the excerpt from Henry Ford's book *My Life and Work*. Then respond to the questions that follow.

EXPLORE THE CONTEXT: Henry Ford is known for inventing the moving assembly line, a manufacturing process that revolutionized production by greatly reducing manufacturing time. In this excerpt, Ford describes how the moving assembly line reduces the time required to produce a piston-rod.

PRIMARY SOURCE: BOOK

❝ Take the development of the piston-rod assembly. Even under the old plan, this operation took only three minutes and did not seem to be one to bother about. There were two benches and twenty-eight men in all; they assembled one hundred seventy-five pistons and rods in a nine-hour day—which means just five seconds over three minutes each. There was no inspection, and many of the piston and rod assemblies came back from the motor assembling line as defective. It is a very simple operation....The foreman, examining the operation, could not discover why it should take as much as three minutes. He analyzed the motions with a stop-watch. He found that four hours out of a nine-hour day were spent in walking. The assembler did not go off anywhere, but he had to shift his feet to gather in his materials and to push away his finished piece. In the whole task, each man performed six operations. The foreman devised a new plan; he split the operation into three divisions, put a slide on the bench and three men on each side of it, and an inspector at the end. Instead of one man performing the whole operation, one man then performed only one third of the operation—he performed only as much as he could do without shifting his feet. They cut down the squad from twenty-eight to fourteen men. The former record for twenty-eight men was one hundred seventy-five assemblies a day. Now seven men turn out twenty-six hundred assemblies in eight hours. It is not necessary to calculate the savings there! ❞

—Henry Ford, *My Life and Work*, 1922

1 **DETERMINING MEANING** Based on the context in which it is used, what does Ford mean by the word *slide*?

_____

_____

VOCABULARY

piston-rod: a critical part of a car that helps power the car's engine

defective: flawed; malfunctioning; unable to be used

foreman: a worker who supervises other workers and is in charge of operations

devised: came up with; invented; developed

2 **DETERMINING CENTRAL IDEAS** What two major changes did Ford make to the manufacturing process to reduce manufacturing time?

_____

_____

_____

_____

3 **ANALYZING INDIVIDUALS** Based on his actions in the excerpt, what words would you use to describe the foreman? For example, is he careless? Emotional? Anxious? Explain why the traits you chose accurately describe the foreman.

_____

_____

_____

_____

4 **EVALUATING** Would you want to work in Ford's factory? Why or why not?

_____

_____

_____

5 **COMPARING AND CONTRASTING** Given the technological advancements that have occurred in the past century, how might Ford's factory today look different from Ford's factory as he describes it in the excerpt?

_____

_____

_____

6 **ANALYZING CHANGE** Manufacturing jobs today are often outsourced to other countries where the cost of labor is lower. Do you think Ford would have outsourced some or all of his manufacturing if he had been able to do so? Why or why not?

_____

_____

_____

_____

ESSENTIAL QUESTION

In what ways do people cope with the problem of scarcity?

My Notes

_____

_____

_____

_____

_____

_____

_____

_____

_____

_____

_____

_____

_____

_____

① Think About It

Review the Supporting Questions that you developed at the beginning of the unit. Review the evidence that you gathered in Chapter 1. Were you able to answer each Supporting Question?

If there was not enough evidence to answer your Supporting Questions, what additional evidence do you think you need to consider?

_____

_____

_____

② Organize Your Evidence

Fill in the chart below to summarize what you have learned about scarcity.

What causes scarcity?	
How does scarcity affect producers?	
How does scarcity affect consumers?	
What can people do to ensure economic growth despite the problem of scarcity?	
How can people use economic models to help them deal with the problem of scarcity?	

3 Talk About It

Work in a small group. Talk with your group and compare and contrast the information you included in your chart. What is scarcity? How does it affect consumers? How does it affect producers?

4 Write About It

Choose one of the topics from the chart. Write a paragraph explaining the topic in more depth. Include an example in your paragraph.

_____

_____

_____

_____

_____

_____

_____

_____

5 Connect to the Essential Question

Interview a member of your community who must cope with the problem of scarcity. For example, you might interview a local business owner, a government worker, or even the principal of your school. Before the interview, come up with a list of questions to ask. Be sure to incorporate questions that relate to the topics in the Organize Your Evidence chart. Take detailed notes during the interview. Use your notes to create a presentation that summarizes the interview and explains how the person you interviewed copes with the problem of scarcity. If your interviewee approves, you may want to record the interview and include audio or video clips in your presentation. Rehearse your presentation and share your findings with your class.

CITIZENSHIP
TAKE ACTION

MAKE CONNECTIONS Think about how scarcity affects your city, county, or state. For example, is there a shortage of affordable housing? Are there parts of the city that are inaccessible without a car? Do some people have to travel long distances to find grocery stores with healthy food options? After you have identified a form of scarcity in your city, county, or state, research the reasons for this type of scarcity. Consider whether this form of scarcity is the result of problems with the WHAT, HOW, or FOR WHOM decisions made by producers and government in your region. For instance, if there is a shortage of housing because resources are being used to develop a new mall, this is a problem with the WHAT decision; on the other hand, if there is plenty of housing, but it is all very expensive, the problem stems from the FOR WHOM decision.

After you have finished your research, come up with a solution for the problem. Be sure to consider the financial implications of your proposed solution, as well as who might be opposed to your idea. It may help to use a decision-making grid or a cost-benefit analysis as you weigh several options. When you have decided on the best solution, create a petition that describes the problem and your proposed solution. Acquire signatures for your petition, and then send it to a government official or business who can help implement your solution.

Understanding Markets

In this unit, you will learn how markets are structured, how they operate, and the factors that influence the choices buyers and sellers make. Read the Essential Questions for each of the four chapters in this unit and think about how they will help you understand markets.

TALK ABOUT IT

Select one Essential Question from each chapter in this unit and discuss it with a partner. What type of information would you need to know in order to answer it? For example, to understand how prices are determined, you must know how the laws of supply and demand work.

DIRECTIONS: Write down two Supporting Questions for each chapter that will help you understand one or more of the Essential Questions in the chapter.

Chapter 4 Demand
ESSENTIAL QUESTIONS

- *How does demand help societies determine WHAT, HOW, and FOR WHOM to produce?*
- *What are the causes of a change in demand?*

MY RESEARCH QUESTIONS

Supporting Question 1:

_____

_____

Supporting Question 2:

_____

_____

Chapter 5 Supply
ESSENTIAL QUESTIONS

- *What are the basic differences between supply and demand?*
- *Why is the production function useful for making business decisions?*
- *How do companies determine the most profitable way to operate?*

MY RESEARCH QUESTIONS

Supporting Question 1:

_____

_____

Supporting Question 2:

_____

_____

Chapter 6 Prices
ESSENTIAL QUESTIONS

- *How do prices help determine WHAT, HOW, and FOR WHOM to produce?*
- *What factors affect prices?*

MY RESEARCH QUESTIONS

Supporting Question 1:

_____

_____

Supporting Question 2:

_____

_____

Chapter 7 Market Structures
ESSENTIAL QUESTIONS

- *How do varying market structures impact prices in a market economy?*
- *Why do markets fail?*
- *How does the government attempt to correct market failures?*

Supporting Question 1:

_____

_____

Supporting Question 2:

_____

_____

INDEPENDENT INQUIRY ACTIVITIES
Chapters 4, 5, and 7

For Chapters 4, 5, and 7, your teacher may ask you to conduct a research project using the Research Questions you have developed above. For these independent inquiry projects, you will follow these steps.

1. Research the answers to your Supporting Questions using online and library resources in addition to the Student Edition text. Analyze the primary and secondary sources you have located and take notes.
2. Select a method to report your findings, such as a research paper, an oral presentation, or a visual essay. Prepare your findings and submit them to your teacher or share them with your class.
3. To conclude, think of ways you could take action based on your findings. Choose one way to get involved.

GUIDED INQUIRY ACTIVITY
Chapter 6

This unit's guided inquiry activity focuses on Chapter 6 *Prices*. In the guided inquiry activity, you will follow the same process as the independent activities; however, primary sources and questions about these sources and the Student Edition text are provided to help guide you through the inquiry process.

Reread the Supporting Questions you developed for Chapter 6 as you prepare to search for evidence in the Student Edition text.

How Prices Work

DIRECTIONS: Search for evidence in Chapter 6, Lesson 1, to help you answer the following questions.

1 **DESCRIBING** How do prices act as a signal to both producers and consumers?

_____

_____

_____

_____

2 **SUMMARIZING** What are the advantages of prices?

_____

_____

3 **DIFFERENTIATING** How does the price system differ from rationing?

_____

_____

_____

4A HISTORY During the energy shortage of the 1970s, what system did the U.S. government use to ration gasoline?

_____

_____

_____

4B **ANALYZING EVENTS** Do you think this system was fair? Why or why not?

_____

_____

_____

_____

ESSENTIAL QUESTION

How do prices help determine WHAT, HOW, and FOR WHOM to produce?

As you gather evidence to answer the Essential Question, think about:

- how prices help individuals, businesses, and markets determine WHAT, HOW, and FOR WHOM to produce.
- the advantages of a price system.
- four major problems with rationing.

My Notes

_____

_____

_____

_____

_____

_____

_____

5 ANALYZING ISSUES Four common problems associated with rationing are listed in the left-hand column. Imagine that the government has decided to ration Internet usage in schools. How could each of the four problems manifest itself in this situation?

Perceived Fairness	
Administrative Expense	
Distorted Incentives	
Abuse and Misuse	

6 EVALUATING Is rationing ever justified? If so, under what circumstances? If not, why not?

_____

_____

_____

7 EXPLAINING EFFECTS Fossil fuels, such as coal and gas, are nonrenewable resources. When we run out, we will have to find alternative sources of energy. How might the steady depletion of fossil fuels affect the allocation of resources?

_____

_____

_____

_____

_____

Where Do Prices Come From?

Copyright © McGraw-Hill Education; TEXT: Roberts, Russell. "Where Do Prices Come From?" Library of Economics and Liberty, June 4, 2007. http://www.econlib.org/library/Columns/y2007/Robertsprices.html.

ESSENTIAL QUESTION

How do prices help determine WHAT, HOW, and FOR WHOM to produce?

VOCABULARY

jumble: mess

equate: equal; match

DIRECTIONS: Read the excerpt from an article by economist Russell Roberts. Then answer the questions that follow.

EXPLORE THE CONTEXT: Russell Roberts is an economist, author, and professor. He also hosts a podcast about economics. This excerpt comes from an article called "Where Do Prices Come From?" In the article, Roberts examines the factors that influence prices.

SECONDARY SOURCE: ARTICLE

"There's a certain predictability to prices. An orderliness. It needn't be that way. Prices could be a random jumble, high one day low the next. On some days, movie tickets could cost more than oxford button down shirts, oranges more than a quart of milk. What is the source of that order? Where do prices come from? The answer at first, seems obvious. The seller sets the price. But if you've ever tried to sell anything, you know that it's not really true.... [I]f you choose a price that's too high, you won't sell it.... Prices adjust to equate how much people want to buy with how much they want to sell. And if people want to buy more than they did before, prices rise. If people want to sell more than they did before, prices fall. Supply and demand. Buyers are competing with each other. Sellers are competing with each other. The prices we observe emerge from this competition."

—Russell Roberts, "Where Do Prices Come From?," June 4, 2007

1 ANALYZING CENTRAL IDEAS According to Roberts, how are prices ultimately determined?

_____

_____

_____

2A IDENTIFYING EFFECTS How are prices affected by competition?

_____

_____

_____

2B **DRAWING CONCLUSIONS** Today, many stores sell identical products. As a result, some stores offer to price match, or sell an identical item for the same price as a competitor. Why would a store offer to price match if it means selling a product for less than the listed price?

_____

_____

_____

_____

3 **INFERRING** Why might individuals feel that "prices could be a random jumble"?

_____

_____

4 **INTEGRATING INFORMATION** In May, a department store is selling swimsuits for $60 each. In September, the same swimsuits are selling for $30 each. According to Roberts, why would the department store reduce the price of swimsuits in September?

_____

_____

_____

_____

_____

5A **ANALYZING INFORMATION** Why would one 24 x 36 inch painting in a gallery be priced at $5,000 and another at $50? Assume a similar number of hours and materials at similar costs went into each painting.

_____

_____

_____

5B **EVALUATING** Who decides the quality of a piece of art? How does this relate to the price of a piece of art?

_____

_____

_____

_____

The Effects of Prices

DIRECTIONS: Search for evidence in Chapter 6, Lesson 2, to help you answer the following questions.

1 **ANALYZING CENTRAL IDEAS** Why is price a compromise between buyers and sellers?

_____

_____

_____

_____

_____

ESSENTIAL QUESTION

What factors affect prices?

As you gather evidence to answer the Essential Question, think about:

- how price can affect a buyer's decision to buy a product and a seller's decision to produce a product.
- how changes in supply and demand affect price.
- how prices adjust in competitive markets.

2A **DRAWING CONCLUSIONS** A pizza restaurant is willing to offer 50 pizzas at a price of $22 per pizza. Buyers are willing to buy 10 pizzas at this price. Will there be a surplus or a shortage of pizzas at the end of the day? Why?

_____

_____

_____

My Notes

_____

_____

_____

_____

_____

_____

2B **INFERRING** The pizza restaurant decides to lower the price of a pizza to $15. Just before closing time, the restaurant sells its last pizza. What can you infer about the $15 price?

_____

_____

_____

2C **PREDICTING** What do you think would have happened if the pizza restaurant had decided to lower the price of a pizza to $10 instead of $15?

_____

_____

_____

3 **IDENTIFYING EFFECTS** Fill in the table to describe how each event will affect supply, demand, or both. Then explain how the price will change. The first one has been done for you as an example.

Event	Effect	Price Change
A hailstorm destroys most of the corn growing in several Midwestern states.	The supply of corn will decrease.	The price of corn will increase.
A toy company heavily advertises stuffed animal versions of the main characters from a popular children's movie.		
A large oil shipment spills in the Pacific Ocean right after a major manufacturing company begins using new machines that rely on oil.		
Automated bots purchase thousands of tickets to a popular concert minutes after tickets go on sale.		
The government releases a report showing that cake sold at a national bakery has been making people ill.		

4A **INTERPRETING CHARTS/GRAPHS** Review the supply and demand schedule for school sweatshirts. Then use the information provided to create a supply and demand curve.

Price	Quantity Demanded	Quantity Supplied	Surplus/Shortage
$100	0	45	45
$60	15	35	20
$50	20	30	10
$40	25	25	0
$30	30	20	−10
$20	35	10	−25
$10	45	0	−45

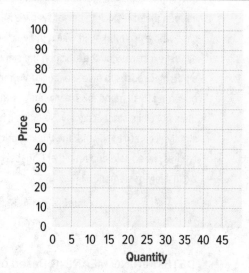

4B **INTEGRATING INFORMATION** Based on the supply and demand schedule and/or the supply and demand curve in question 4A, what is the equilibrium price and quantity for school sweatshirts?

Copyright © McGraw-Hill Education; TEXT: Marshall, Alfred. 1890. Principles of Economics. London: Macmillan and Co., Ltd.

ESSENTIAL QUESTION
What factors affect prices?

Principles of Economics

DIRECTIONS: Read the excerpt from *Principles of Economics* by Alfred Marshall. Then answer the questions that follow.

EXPLORE THE CONTEXT: There is nothing more crucial to the study of economics than the relationship between supply and demand, which ultimately determines the equilibrium price. Economist Alfred Marshall uses the simple analogy of scissors cutting paper to explain how utility, which affects demand, and cost of production, which affects supply, interact to determine price.

PRIMARY SOURCE: BOOK

66 We might as reasonably dispute whether it is the upper or the under blade of a pair of scissors that cuts a piece of paper, as whether value [price] is governed by utility or cost of production. It is true that when one blade is held still, and the cutting is effected by moving the other, we may say with careless brevity that the cutting is done by the second; but the statement is not strictly accurate, and is to be excused only so long as it claims to be merely a popular and not a strictly scientific account of what happens.

In the same way, when a thing already made has to be sold, the price which people will be willing to pay for it will be governed by their desire to have it, together with the amount they can afford to spend on it. Their desire to have it depends partly on the chance that, if they do not buy it, they will be able to get another thing like it at as low a price: this depends on the causes that govern the supply of it, and this again upon cost of production. But it may so happen that the stock to be sold is practically fixed. This, for instance, is the case with a fish market, in which the value of fish for the day is governed almost exclusively by the stock on the slabs in relation to the demand: and if a person chooses to take the stock for granted, and say that the price is governed by demand, his brevity may perhaps be excused so long as he does not claim strict accuracy. So again it may be pardonable, but it is not strictly accurate to say that the varying prices which the same rare book fetches, when sold and resold at Christie's auction room, are governed exclusively by demand. 99

—Alfred Marshall, *Principles of Economics*, 1890

VOCABULARY

dispute: argue

utility: usefulness

brevity: conciseness; simplification

governed: determined

1 **DETERMINING MEANING** Based on the context in which it is used, what is the meaning of the word *effected*?

_____

_____

2A **DESCRIBING** How is the price of a product determined? Use the scissors analogy to explain the process.

_____

_____

_____

_____

2B **ANALYZING TEXT STRUCTURE** Why do you think Marshall decided to incorporate the scissors analogy into his discussion of supply and demand?

_____

_____

_____

_____

3 **INFERRING** How does price act as a balance between supply and demand?

_____

_____

4 **ANALYZING POINT OF VIEW** Tim goes to the grocery store every day for one month. He determines that the average price for apples during that month is $3 per pound. The next month, however, the average price for apples is $6 per pound. Tim concludes that the price rose because demand for apples increased. How would Marshall respond to Tim's conclusion?

_____

_____

_____

_____

5 **COMPARING** According to Marshall, how are the prices for fish at a fish market and the prices for rare books at an auction house similar?

_____

_____

_____

Social Goals, Prices, and Market Efficiency

DIRECTIONS: Search for evidence in Chapter 6, Lesson 3, to help you answer the following questions.

1A DETERMINING CENTRAL IDEAS What is a price ceiling? What is a price floor?

_____

_____

_____

1B EXPLAINING EFFECTS How can a price ceiling create a shortage? How can a price floor create a surplus?

_____

_____

_____

_____

_____

2 INFERRING Under what circumstances might the government use price controls?

_____

_____

_____

_____

_____

_____

3 ANALYZING ISSUES How can the goal of economic equity conflict with the goal of economic efficiency?

_____

_____

_____

ESSENTIAL QUESTION

What factors affect prices?

As you gather evidence to answer the Essential Question, think about:

- how markets are affected by price ceilings and price floors.

- why government interference in the market may lead to conflicting economic goals.

- events that may cause markets to "talk."

My Notes

_____

_____

_____

_____

_____

_____

4 **EVALUATING** The Student Edition text uses rent control and sugar prices as examples of price ceilings and price floors. Use information from the text to fill in the graphic organizer.

	Example	Objective	Problems
Price Ceiling	Rent control in major U.S. cities		
Price Floor	Sugar prices after the 2008 Farm Act		

5 **RELATING EVENTS** Congress announces a new foreign trade deal. Shortly after, the markets begin "talking." Stock prices rise, and the prices of gold and oil drop. What are the markets saying?

_____

_____

_____

ESSENTIAL QUESTION
What factors affect prices?

The Pernicious Effects of Price Controls

DIRECTIONS: Read the excerpt from an article written by economist Valentin Petkantchin. Then answer the questions that follow.

EXPLORE THE CONTEXT: Although most people think that price ceilings benefit consumers by ensuring lower prices, French economist Valentin Petkantchin disagrees. In this article, he discusses the ways that price ceilings can actually harm consumers.

SECONDARY SOURCE: ARTICLE

"It is quite easy to comprehend how artificially high prices penalize consumers, but the damage caused by artificially low prices is less obvious. Is it not in consumers' interest to pay less for products and services?

Such price controls also have pernicious effects. First, lower prices lead consumers to buy more, thereby raising demand. But lower prices also make production and investment in regulated goods or services less lucrative. Resources and production factors are thereby likely to leave a sector, or a country, where such controls apply.

Unless other measures are imposed, such as subsidizing affected producers or investors, imposing a ceiling price will make a regulated good or service become scarce. Long lineups start to form, preventing consumers from getting as much as they want. Generally speaking, lower prices may benefit certain consumers in the short term but, by penalizing producers, they end up causing consumers damage in the long run."

— Valentin Petkantchin, "The Pernicious Effects of Price Controls," Montreal Economic Institute, 2006

VOCABULARY

penalize: hurt

pernicious: harmful

lucrative: profitable; rewarding

imposed: put in place

subsidizing: paying part of the costs

1 **DETERMINING MEANING** Petkantchin describes the harmful effects of "artificially high prices" and "artificially low prices." What does he mean by the word *artificial*?

_____

_____

_____

2 SUMMARIZING How are consumers hurt in the long run by price ceilings?

_____

_____

_____

3 ANALYZING TEXT STRUCTURE Petkantchin says that "it is quite easy to comprehend how artificially high prices penalize consumers." Why would Petkantchin begin a discussion of price ceilings (artificially low prices) with this statement about artificially high prices?

_____

_____

_____

_____

_____

4 INFERRING How would subsidizing producers compensate for price controls?

_____

_____

_____

_____

5 IDENTIFYING PERSPECTIVES What might someone who disagrees with Petkantchin argue about price controls?

_____

_____

_____

_____

6 ANALYZING POINT OF VIEW The minimum wage is an example of a price floor, or an artificially high price intended to ensure that workers can earn enough money to support themselves. Do you think Petkantchin would support the minimum wage? Why or why not?

_____

_____

_____

_____

ESSENTIAL QUESTIONS

How do prices help determine WHAT, HOW, and FOR WHOM to produce?

What factors affect prices?

My Notes

_____

_____

_____

_____

_____

_____

_____

_____

_____

_____

_____

_____

_____

_____

1 Think About It

Review the Supporting Questions that you developed at the beginning of the unit. Review the evidence that you gathered in Chapter 6. Were you able to answer each Supporting Question?

If there was not enough evidence to answer your Supporting Questions, what additional evidence do you think you need to consider?

_____

_____

_____

_____

2 Organize Your Evidence

Complete the chart below with information about prices.

How Prices Help Us	
How Demand Affects Prices	
How Supply Affects Prices	
How Government Policies Affect Prices	

3 Talk About It

Work in small groups. Talk with your group and compare and contrast the information you included in your chart. How do prices help us? How do supply and demand affect prices? How do government policies affect prices? Explain your answers.

4 Write About It

Choose one of the topics from the Organize Your Evidence chart. Write a detailed paragraph about that topic. Include specific examples that help your reader understand the importance of prices and/or the factors that affect prices.

_____

_____

_____

_____

_____

_____

_____

_____

_____

5 Connect to the Essential Questions

Imagine that you are going to start your own business. How would you determine the prices for your product? Write a business plan that includes WHAT you would produce, HOW you would produce it, and FOR WHOM you would produce it. Include the prices for the product, why you chose those prices, and the factors that would affect the prices. As you devise your business plan, think about the Essential Questions: _How do prices help determine WHAT, HOW, and FOR WHOM to produce? What factors affect prices?_

CITIZENSHIP
TAKE ACTION

MAKE CONNECTIONS Recall that governments set price controls in order to ensure equity and security for people and businesses. Choose an example of a price control in your state, such as rent control, the state minimum wage, the minimum wage in a specific city, or another price floor or price ceiling. Then research the price control you have selected. Investigate the history of the price control, including why it was enacted, any updates or changes to the law since it was established, and how it has affected consumers and producers in the area. Decide if you support or oppose the price control. Then take action by writing a letter to a local official. In your letter, clearly state your position on the price control and support it with logical reasoning and evidence.

_____

_____

_____

_____

_____

_____

_____

_____

_____

_____

_____

_____

_____

_____

_____

_____

Business and Labor

In this unit, you will learn about the three main types of business organizations: sole proprietorships, partnerships, and corporations. You will also learn how businesses grow and change, and how nonprofit organizations fit into a market economy. Then you will study the history of labor in the United States, including the challenges still facing workers today. Read the Essential Questions for both chapters in this unit and think about how they will help you understand the ways that businesses and workers contribute to the economy.

TALK ABOUT IT

Select one Essential Question from each chapter in this unit and discuss it with a partner. What type of information would you need to know in order to answer it? For example, to understand the role of nonprofit organizations in a market economy, you need to know what a nonprofit organization is and how it functions.

DIRECTIONS: Write down two Supporting Questions for each chapter that will help you understand one or more of the Essential Questions in the chapter.

Chapter 8 Business Organization
ESSENTIAL QUESTIONS

- *How are businesses formed and how do they grow?*

- *How does a market economy support nonprofit organizations?*

MY RESEARCH QUESTIONS

Supporting Question 1:

_____

_____

Supporting Question 2:

_____

_____

Chapter 9 Labor and Wages
ESSENTIAL QUESTIONS

- *What features of the modern labor industry are the result of union action?*

- *What factors lead to higher wages for a worker?*

MY RESEARCH QUESTIONS

Supporting Question 1:

_____

_____

Supporting Question 2:

_____

_____

INDEPENDENT INQUIRY ACTIVITY
Chapter 8

For Chapter 8, your teacher may ask you to conduct a research project using the Research Questions you have developed above. For this independent inquiry project, you will follow these steps.

1. Research the answers to your Supporting Questions using online and library resources in addition to the Student Edition text. Analyze the primary and secondary sources you have located and take notes.
2. Select a method to report your findings, such as a research paper, an oral presentation, or a visual essay. Prepare your findings and submit them to your teacher or share them with your class.
3. To conclude, think of ways you could take action based on your findings. Choose one way to get involved.

GUIDED INQUIRY ACTIVITY
Chapter 9

This unit's guided inquiry activity focuses on Chapter 9 *Labor and Wages*. In the guided inquiry activity, you will follow the same process as the independent activity; however, primary and secondary sources and questions about these sources and the Student Edition text are provided to help guide you through the inquiry process.

Reread the Supporting Questions you developed for Chapter 9 as you prepare to search for evidence in the Student Edition text.

The Labor Movement

DIRECTIONS: Search for evidence in Chapter 9, Lesson 1, to help you answer the following questions.

1 **DIFFERENTIATING** What is the difference between a trade (craft) union and an industrial union?

_____

_____

_____

_____

2 **COMPARING AND CONTRASTING** Fill in the table below to describe the different types of union actions and employer resistance measures.

	What is it?	Action by workers or employers?	Goal/purpose?
Strike			
Boycott			
Picket			
Lockout			
Company Union			

ESSENTIAL QUESTION

What features of the modern labor industry are the result of union action?

As you gather evidence to answer the Essential Question, think about:

- why early unions developed.
- how historical events, such as the Great Depression, affected the labor industry.
- how modern unions are structured.
- why union membership has changed over time.

My Notes

_____

_____

_____

_____

_____

_____

3 RELATING EVENTS Why did the Great Depression encourage more positive attitudes toward unions?

_____

_____

4 CIVICS For each labor law below, describe the results or changes that occurred after the law was passed.

Labor Law		Result of Labor Law
The National Labor Relations Act (Wagner Act)	→	
The Fair Labor Standards Act	→	
The Labor-Management Relations Act (Taft-Hartley Act)	→	
The Labor-Management Reporting and Disclosure Act (Landrum-Griffin Act)	→	

5 MAKING DECISIONS Would you want to work in a state with a right-to-work law? Why or why not?

_____

_____

_____

6 EVALUATING Do you think closed shops and union shops are fair to workers? Do you think they are fair to employers? Why or why not?

_____

_____

_____

_____

_____

ESSENTIAL QUESTION

What features of the modern labor industry are the result of union action?

What Does the Working Man Want?

DIRECTIONS: Read the excerpt from a speech by Samuel Gompers. Then answer the questions that follow.

EXPLORE THE CONTEXT: In the early 1800s, many Americans worked ten to fourteen hours per day. By the mid-1800s, a movement to limit the workday to eight hours had begun to take shape. Laws were passed to shorten the workday, but loopholes allowed employers to extend the day past the legal limit. In 1886, Samuel Gompers was elected president of the American Federation of Labor (AFL). Each year, the AFL targeted one industry and used strikes to win an eight-hour workday in that industry. This 1890 speech by Samuel Gompers was part of his campaign for the eight-hour workday.

PRIMARY SOURCE: SPEECH

❝In all industries where the hours of labor are long, there you will find the least development of the power of invention. Where the hours of labor are long, men are cheap, and where men are cheap there is no necessity for invention. How can you expect a man to work ten or twelve or fourteen hours at his calling and then devote any time to the invention of a machine or discovery of a new principle or force? If he be so fortunate as to be able to read a paper he will fall asleep before he has read through the second or third line.

Why, when you reduce the hours of labor, say an hour a day, just think what it means. Suppose men who work ten hours a day had the time lessened to nine, or men who work nine hours a day have it reduced to eight hours; what does it mean? It means millions of golden hours and opportunities for thought. Some men might say you will go to sleep. Well, some men might sleep sixteen hours a day; the ordinary man might try that, but he would soon find he could not do it long. He would have to do something. He would probably go to the theater one night, to a concert another night, but could not do that every night. He would probably become interested in some study and the hours that have been taken for manual labor are devoted to mental labor, and the mental labor of one hour will produce for him more wealth than the physical labor of a dozen hours.

I maintain that this is a true proposition—that men under the short-hour system not only have opportunity to improve themselves, but to make a greater degree of prosperity for their employers. Why, my friends, how is it in China, how is it in Spain, how is it in India and Russia, how is it in Italy? Cast your eye throughout the universe and observe the industry that forces nature to yield up its fruits to man's necessities, and you will find that where the hours of labor are the shortest the progress of invention in machinery and the prosperity of the people are the greatest. ❞

—Samuel Gompers, "What Does the Working Man Want?," May 1, 1890

VOCABULARY

proposition: proposal; suggestion

prosperity: wealth

yield: give

1 **DETERMINING MEANING** What does Gompers mean by the term *mental labor*?

_____

_____

2 **SUMMARIZING** According to Gompers, how will a shorter workday benefit society as a whole?

_____

_____

_____

3 **ANALYZING TEXT STRUCTURE** Why does Gompers discuss the possibility that workers with a shorter workday might spend more time sleeping, going to the theater, or attending concerts? What is the purpose of this section of his speech?

_____

_____

_____

_____

_____

_____

4 **INFERRING** Based on the context, what can you infer about the workday in China, Spain, India, Russia, and Italy? What can you infer about invention in these countries?

_____

_____

5 **ANALYZING INFORMATION** Studies show that workers in Mexico work the most hours, at an average of 2,255 hours per year, while workers in Germany work the fewest hours, at an average of 1,363 hours per year. At the same time, the GDP per capita of Mexico is about $8,000, and the GDP per capita of Germany is about $42,000. Based on this information, would you recommend increasing work hours in order to increase GDP per capita? Why or why not?

_____

_____

_____

_____

Wages and Labor Disputes

DIRECTIONS: Search for evidence in Chapter 9, Lesson 2, to help you answer the following questions.

1 INFERRING Why might workers with more skills and education earn higher wages?

_____

_____

_____

2 ANALYZING IDEAS Why don't workers in one category of labor compete with workers in other categories of labor?

_____

_____

_____

3 DRAWING CONCLUSIONS Based on the market theory of wage determination, why would a surgeon earn a lot more money than a teacher?

_____

_____

_____

_____

4 EVALUATING Based on signaling theory and the theory of negotiated wages, which worker is likely to have the highest salary? Why?

Worker 1: a recent college graduate who has been with the same company for one year and has joined a union

Worker 2: a worker with a college degree who belongs to a union and has worked at the same company for twenty years

Worker 3: a high school graduate who is seeking his first job and does not intend to join a union

_____

_____

_____

ESSENTIAL QUESTION

What factors lead to higher wages for a worker?

As you gather evidence to answer the Essential Question, think about:

- how the four categories of labor differ.
- the similarities and differences among the various theories of wage determination.
- how labor disputes are resolved.
- the advantages and disadvantages of having a minimum wage.

My Notes

_____

_____

_____

_____

_____

_____

5 **INTEGRATING INFORMATION** There are many methods of resolving labor disputes. Fill in the chart below with information about each method.

	What is it?	Who is involved?	How is the dispute resolved?
Collective Bargaining			
Mediation			
Arbitration			
Fact-Finding			
Injunction			
Seizure			
Presidential Intervention			

6 **ANALYZING ISSUES** Some union contracts contain a no-strike clause that prohibits workers from striking. Do you think it is fair for contracts to include this clause? Why or why not?

_____

_____

_____

_____

ESSENTIAL QUESTION

What factors lead to higher wages for a worker?

Remarks and a Question-and-Answer Session With Reporters on the Air Traffic Controllers Strike

DIRECTIONS: Read President Ronald Reagan's statement. Then answer the questions that follow.

EXPLORE THE CONTEXT: In 1981, members of the Professional Air Traffic Controllers Organization demanded increased wages and a shorter work week. The Federal Aviation Administration (FAA) refused to meet the air traffic controllers' demands. As a result, at 7:00 AM on August 3, 1981, almost 13,000 air traffic controllers went on strike, forcing airlines to cancel 7,000 flights. At 10:55 AM, President Reagan read an official statement to the press. He claimed that the air traffic controllers were in violation of an oath they had taken when they first accepted their positions, and he threatened to fire any workers who did not return to their jobs. Although some workers went back to work, President Reagan ultimately fired over 11,000 air traffic controllers.

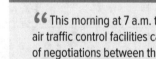

PRIMARY SOURCE: OFFICIAL STATEMENT

66 This morning at 7 a.m. the union representing those who man America's air traffic control facilities called a strike. This was the culmination of 7 months of negotiations between the Federal Aviation Administration and the union. At one point in these negotiations agreement was reached and signed by both sides, granting a $40 million increase in salaries and benefits. This is twice what other government employees can expect. It was granted in recognition of the difficulties inherent in the work these people perform. Now, however, the union demands are 17 times what had been agreed to—$681 million. This would impose a tax burden on their fellow citizens which is unacceptable....

Let me make one thing plain. I respect the right of workers in the private sector to strike. Indeed, as president of my own union, I led the first strike ever called by that union. I guess I'm maybe the first one to ever hold this office who is a lifetime member of an AFL-CIO union. But we cannot compare labor-management relations in the private sector with government. Government cannot close down the assembly line. It has to provide without interruption the protective services which are government's reason for being.

It was in recognition of this that the Congress passed a law forbidding strikes by government employees against the public safety. Let me read the solemn oath taken by each of these employees, a sworn affidavit, when they accepted their jobs: "I am not participating in any strike against the Government of the United States or any agency thereof, and I will not so participate while an employee of the Government of the United States or any agency thereof."

It is for this reason that I must tell those who fail to report for duty this morning they are in violation of the law, and if they do not report for work within 48 hours, they have forfeited their jobs and will be terminated. 99

—President Ronald Reagan, "Remarks and a Question-and-Answer Session With Reporters on the Air Traffic Controllers Strike," August 3, 1981

VOCABULARY

culmination: climax; conclusion

impose: inflict; cause

solemn: formal; legal

affidavit: oath; pledge; promise

forfeited: given up

terminated: fired

1 IDENTIFYING PERSPECTIVES How does President Reagan feel about unions?

_____

_____

2 DETERMINING CENTRAL IDEAS According to President Reagan, what is the purpose of government?

_____

_____

3 EVALUATING EVIDENCE Does President Reagan make a strong argument for his decision to fire workers who do not return to their jobs? Why or why not?

_____

_____

_____

_____

4 CITING TEXT EVIDENCE How much would it cost to meet the air traffic controllers' demands? How much money did the Federal Aviation Administration offer during the negotiations?

_____

_____

5 ANALYZING TEXT STRUCTURE Why would President Reagan mention the tax burden that would result from meeting the workers' demands?

_____

_____

_____

_____

6 ANALYZING ISSUES President Reagan says that government employees should not be allowed to strike. Are there other workers who are so critical to society that they should also not be allowed to strike? If so, which workers? Why?

_____

_____

_____

_____

Employment Trends and Issues

DIRECTIONS: Search for evidence in Chapter 9, Lesson 3, to help you answer the following questions.

1 **IDENTIFYING CAUSES** Fill in the chart below to show reasons for the decline of union influence.

ESSENTIAL QUESTION

What factors lead to higher wages for a worker?

As you gather evidence to answer the Essential Question, think about:

- why union influence has declined.
- why women are often paid less than men.
- the advantages and disadvantages of the minimum wage.

Decline of Union Influence

My Notes

2 **ANALYZING IDEAS** What is a two-tier wage system? Do you think this system is fair to workers? Why or why not?

3 **ANALYZING ISSUES** Choose one reason that women are often paid less than men. Suggest at least one way the problem could be addressed to help women earn higher wages.

_____

_____

_____

_____

The graph below shows the distribution of women and men in various occupations. Use the graph to answer questions 4A and 4B.

Distribution of Women and Men by Occupation

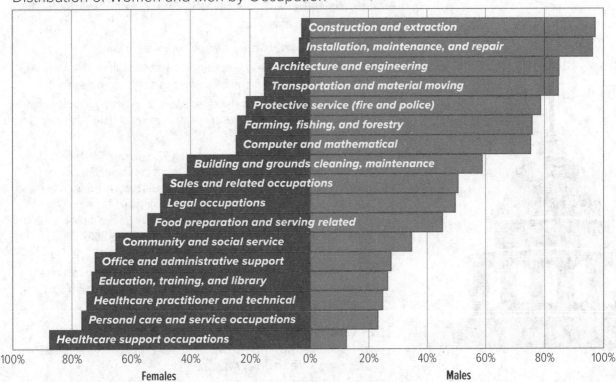

Source: Bureau of Labor Statistics, 2016

4A **INTERPRETING CHARTS/GRAPHS** Which two occupations have the most even distribution of men and women? Which occupation has the most women? Which occupation has the most men?

_____

_____

4B **CONSTRUCTING HYPOTHESES** Why do you think some occupations tend to attract more men than women? Why might other occupations tend to attract more women than men?

_____

_____

_____

Copyright © McGraw-Hill Education; TEXT: U.S. Cong. House. Congressional Record: Proceedings and Debates of the 113th Congress, 1st sess. Bill. 46th ed. Vol. 159. Daily Edition. Washington D.C.: U.S. Government Printing Office, 2013. H1849.

ESSENTIAL QUESTION

What factors lead to higher wages for a worker?

Equal Pay Day

DIRECTIONS: Read the statements from two House of Representatives members from California. Then respond to the questions that follow.

EXPLORE THE CONTEXT: On April 9, 2013, Congress celebrated Equal Pay Day, the day when women's wages catch up with men's wages for the previous year. In honor of the occasion, several members of the House of Representatives expressed their support for a bill that would continue to rectify the gender-based wage gap.

PRIMARY SOURCE: CONGRESSIONAL RECORD

Representative Barbara Lee:

"Mr. Speaker, today we rise in support of Equal Pay Day.

Equal Pay Day symbolizes when more than 3 months into the year women's wages finally catch up with what men were paid in the previous year.

It's unconscionable that women today continue to be blatantly discriminated against in the workforce in terms of their pay and the treatment that they receive.

In 2011, women working full time made only 77 cents to every dollar made by men over the course of a year. The landscape is even worse for women of color. In 2011, African American women earned 64 cents to every dollar earned by white males, and for Latinas it was only 55 cents and 42 cents in my home State of California. On average, the wage gap costs women roughly $11,000 annually, and at this rate the wage gap will not close until 2057. Can you imagine that, 2057?…

Women and their families cannot afford to continue paying the cost of our inaction in the face of injustice. I hope the Speaker will bring this bill to the floor right away."

Representative Ami Bera:

"Mr. Speaker, today I rise to celebrate Equal Pay Day as we mark the 50th anniversary of the Equal Pay Act.

In the last 50 years, women have gone into space and off to war. They've led Fortune 500 companies and served on the Supreme Court. They've been elected Speaker of the House and run for President; yet women still earn only 77 cents for every dollar a man earns.

In the Sacramento area, women lose approximately $2.2 billion each year because of this pay gap. Now, that's unacceptable and as a father it's personal. I want my daughter to grow up in a country where her gender is not a barrier to her success.

And the wage gap doesn't just hurt women; it hurts families, businesses, and communities. Women are now nearly half of our workforce, and oftentimes it's up to women to put food on the table and provide for their families.…

It's time for us to finish what President Kennedy started 50 years ago and what women have been working to achieve for more than a century and make equal pay a reality for millions of Americans."

—"Equal Pay Day," Congressional Record, House of Representatives, 2013

VOCABULARY

unconscionable: unacceptable; appalling

blatantly: obviously; openly

landscape: situation; outlook

1 **CITING TEXT EVIDENCE** What statistic is cited by both representatives? Why do you think they both chose to include this statistic in their speech?

_____

_____

_____

2 **DIFFERENTIATING** In what ways do the two arguments differ?

_____

_____

_____

_____

_____

_____

3 **EVALUATING EVIDENCE** Which argument do you find more convincing? Why?

_____

_____

_____

_____

_____

4 **ANALYZING TEXT STRUCTURE** Representative Lee claims that at the current rate of change, the wage gap will not close until 2057. Then she asks, "Can you imagine that, 2057?" This is a rhetorical question because Lee does not expect anyone to answer her. Why does she include this question if she does not expect an answer?

_____

_____

5 **ANALYZING POINT OF VIEW** Representative Lee uses strong language to strengthen her argument. Find at least one example of her use of strong language and explain why it makes her argument more convincing.

_____

_____

_____

_____

ESSENTIAL QUESTIONS

What features of the modern labor industry are the result of union action?

What factors lead to higher wages for a worker?

My Notes

_____

_____

_____

_____

_____

_____

_____

_____

_____

_____

_____

_____

_____

① Think About It

Review the Supporting Questions that you developed at the beginning of the unit. Review the evidence that you gathered in Chapter 9. Were you able to answer each Supporting Question?

If there was not enough evidence to answer your Supporting Questions, what additional evidence do you think you need to consider?

_____

_____

_____

② Organize Your Evidence

Fill in the chart below to summarize what you have learned about unions, labor, and wages.

Types of unions	
Ways that unions fight management	
Ways that management fights workers	
Ways to resolve labor disputes	
Laws that protect workers and union activity	
Laws that protect management and firms	
Factors that increase wages for a worker	
Factors that decrease wages for women	

3 Talk About It

Work in a small group. Talk with your group and compare and contrast the information you included in your chart. How do workers, management, and government interact? How are wages determined in our society?

4 Write About It

Choose one of the topics from the chart. Write a paragraph that discusses the topic in more depth. Be sure to include specific details from the Student Edition text.

_____

_____

_____

_____

_____

_____

_____

_____

_____

_____

5 Connect to the Essential Questions

Write and perform a skit in which members of a labor union negotiate with management. Be sure that members of the labor union clearly express what they want from management (e.g. better pay, safer working conditions, shorter hours, etc.) and why they deserve to have their demands met. Management should clearly explain why it does not approve of those demands. Both sides should also explain what will happen if an agreement cannot be reached. The skit should conclude with a logical compromise that both labor and management can accept. As you plan your skit, think about the Essential Questions: *What features of the modern labor industry are the result of union action? What factors lead to higher wages for a worker?*

TAKE ACTION

MAKE CONNECTIONS Think about a problem that affects workers today. For example, you might consider the minimum wage, discrimination, working conditions/safety, or the decline in union membership and influence. Then write a new law that would solve the problem. Be sure your law is clear, practical, and likely to gain voter support. Remember that voters do not only include workers; in order for your law to pass, you need support from businesses and management too.

Once you have written your law, create a campaign that persuades voters to vote for your law in the upcoming election. Remember that voters may not know much about current laws that affect workers, so be sure to provide background information and explain why your law is necessary. Consider the best way to reach your desired audience. For example, you might choose to create a flyer, a poster, a television or radio commercial, or an online advertisement. You might also want to combine several of these mediums.

Money, Banking, and Finance

In this unit, you will learn how money and banking have changed over time. You will also learn how to invest in financial assets, such as stocks and bonds. Read the Essential Questions for both chapters in this unit and think about how they will help you understand money, banking, and investing.

TALK ABOUT IT

Select one Essential Question from each chapter in this unit and discuss it with a partner. What type of information would you need to know in order to answer it? For example, to understand how the Federal Reserve System ("the Fed") improved our banking system, you must first understand the weaknesses of our banking system prior to the establishment of the Fed.

DIRECTIONS: Write down two Supporting Questions for each chapter that will help you understand one or more of the Essential Questions in the chapter.

Chapter 10 Money and Banking
ESSENTIAL QUESTIONS

- *How has money evolved to meet the needs of people everywhere?*
- *How did the creation of the Fed improve our banking system?*
- *How has technology affected the way we use money today?*

MY RESEARCH QUESTIONS

Supporting Question 1:

_____

_____

Supporting Question 2:

_____

_____

_____

Chapter 11 Financial Markets

ESSENTIAL QUESTIONS

- *What is the role of savings in the financial system?*

- *What options are available for investing your money?*

Supporting Question 1:

_____

_____

Supporting Question 2:

_____

_____

INDEPENDENT INQUIRY ACTIVITY

Chapter 11

For Chapter 11, your teacher may ask you to conduct a research project using the Research Questions you have developed above. For this independent inquiry project, you will follow these steps.

1. Research the answers to your Supporting Questions using online and library resources in addition to the Student Edition text. Analyze the primary and secondary sources you have located and take notes.
2. Select a method to report your findings, such as a research paper, an oral presentation, or a visual essay. Prepare your findings and submit them to your teacher or share them with your class.
3. To conclude, think of ways you could take action based on your findings. Choose one way to get involved.

GUIDED INQUIRY ACTIVITY

Chapter 10

This unit's guided inquiry activity focuses on Chapter 10 *Money and Banking*. In the guided inquiry activity, you will follow the same process as the independent activity; however, primary sources and questions about these sources and the Student Edition text are provided to help guide you through the inquiry process.

Reread the Supporting Questions you developed for Chapter 10 as you prepare to search for evidence in the Student Edition text.

Evolution, Functions, and Characteristics of Money

DIRECTIONS: Search for evidence in Chapter 10, Lesson 1, to help you answer the following questions.

1 **COMPARING** What is the difference between commodity money and fiat money?

_____

_____

_____

2 **EXPLAINING EFFECTS** Why did the Continental dollar become nearly worthless?

_____

_____

_____

_____

3 **ANALYZING ISSUES** Why was specie so much more valuable than paper currency?

_____

_____

_____

_____

4 **INFERRING** A shopper sees two brands of spaghetti sauce. One is store brand, and the other is a well-known national brand. Even though the two sauces taste extremely similar, the shopper believes the national brand is more valuable. Based on money's function as a measure of value, which brand would the shopper be willing to pay more for? Why?

_____

_____

_____

ESSENTIAL QUESTION

How has money evolved to meet the needs of people everywhere?

As you gather evidence to answer the Essential Question, think about:

- why money has changed over time.
- the four characteristics and three functions of money.
- how modern money compares to older forms of money.

My Notes

_____

_____

_____

_____

_____

_____

_____

5 **ANALYZING CHANGE** How has our ability to pay for goods and services using smartphone apps affected the portability of money?

_____

_____

_____

6 **IDENTIFYING EFFECTS** Imagine a society in which all transactions, regardless of size, must be made using cash. Credit cards, debit cards, checks, and electronic payments do not exist. For each hypothetical event, decide which characteristic of money is *most* affected and what the effect would be. The first one is done for you as an example.

Event	Which characteristic of money is most affected?	Effect
The Fed removes the penny from circulation.	Divisibility	All prices would have to be rounded to the nearest nickel.
A scientist develops a new chemical that makes paper money last for a minimum of five years.		
The Fed replaces coins with paper currency (e.g. a 1-cent bill, a 5-cent bill, a 10-cent bill, a 25-cent bill).		
The Fed prints one billion additional $1 bills without removing any existing $1 bills from circulation.		

ESSENTIAL QUESTION

How has money evolved to meet the needs of people everywhere?

Description of New Netherlands

DIRECTIONS: Read the excerpt from *Description of New Netherlands* by Adriaen van der Donck. Then answer the questions that follow.

EXPLORE THE CONTEXT: Henry Hudson founded the Dutch colony of New Netherland in the early 1600s. It encompassed parts of the modern states of New York, New Jersey, Connecticut, Pennsylvania, and Delaware. Adriaen van der Donck sailed to North America in 1641. He soon became interested in a conflict between the West India Company and settlers in the part of the colony that is now Manhattan. The West India Company viewed the colony as a source of wealth and treated the settlers as workers with few rights. Van der Donck fought for the settlers' rights and convinced the Dutch government to make New Netherland an official Dutch city. Although a war with England forced the government to break its promise, Van der Donck saw great value in the colony. He wrote *Description of New Netherlands* to encourage people to immigrate to New Netherland. The Dutch ultimately lost New Netherland to the British, but Van der Donck's book remains an excellent source of information about the colony. This excerpt describes how the Native Americans and colonists used wampum, a form of currency made from shells.

PRIMARY SOURCE: BOOK

66 That there should be no miserly desire for the costly metals among the natives, few will believe; still it is true, the use of gold and silver or any metallic coin is unknown among them. The currency which they use in their places to which they resort is called *wampum*, the making and preparing of which is free to all persons. The species are black and white, but the black is worth more by one half than the white. The black wampum is made from conck shells, which are to be taken from the sea, or which are cast ashore from the sea twice a year. They strike off the thin parts of those shells . . . and drill a hole through every piece and string the same on strings, and afterwards sell their strings of wampum in that manner. This is the only article of moneyed medium among the natives, with which any traffic can be driven; and it is also common with us in purchasing necessaries and carrying on our trade; many thousand strings are exchanged every year for peltries near the sea shores where the wampum is only made, and where the peltries are brought for sale. 99

—Adriaen van der Donck, *Description of New Netherlands*, 1649

1 **DETERMINING MEANING** Based on the context in which it is used, what does Van der Donck mean by the word *traffic*?

VOCABULARY

miserly desire for the costly metals: self-serving wish to accumulate valuable silver and gold

resort: turn to; use as an alternative

article of moneyed medium: object used for purchasing

necessaries: necessities; items that fulfill basic needs

peltries: animal pelts or furs

2 **SUMMARIZING** How do the Native Americans turn shells into wampum?

_____

_____

3 **ANALYZING IDEAS** Is wampum a form of commodity money or a form of fiat money? Why?

_____

4 **INTEGRATING INFORMATION** Review the four characteristics of money. Decide if wampum possesses each characteristic. Explain why or why not.

Portability	
Durability	
Divisibility	
Scarcity	

5 **INFERRING** The text says that black wampum "is worth more by one half than the white." Based on what you know about supply and demand, as well as the four characteristics of money, what can you infer about why black wampum is more valuable than white wampum?

_____

6 **DRAWING CONCLUSIONS** Review the three functions of money. Does wampum serve each of these functions? Why or why not?

_____

_____

_____

_____

_____

7 **EVALUATING** Would wampum be an effective form of money in today's society? Why or why not?

_____

_____

_____

_____

The Development of Modern Banking

DIRECTIONS: Search for evidence in Chapter 10, Lesson 2, to help you answer the following questions.

1 **CONTRASTING** How do state banks differ from national banks?

_____

_____

_____

2 **IDENTIFYING EFFECTS** Prior to the Civil War, banks were allowed to print their own currency. What problems resulted from this practice?

_____

_____

_____

_____

_____

_____

3 **ANALYZING IDEAS** How did the federal government use economic incentives to force state banks to become part of the National Banking System?

_____

_____

_____

4 **SUMMARIZING** What are some advantages of the gold standard? What are some disadvantages?

_____

_____

_____

_____

_____

_____

ESSENTIAL QUESTION

How did the creation of the Fed improve our banking system?

As you gather evidence to answer the Essential Question, think about:

- why the National Banking System was created.
- how the Federal Reserve System strengthened our banking system.
- the advantages and disadvantages of the gold standard.

My Notes

_____

_____

_____

_____

_____

_____

_____

5 HISTORY Fill in the time line to show the history of banking in the United States.

| Congress prints paper currency for the first time. The new currency is called "greenbacks." | | | | President Roosevelt denies the gold standard to the American people, and the Banking Act of 1933 creates the FDIC. |

1861 1863 1865   1900   1913   1929 1933   1971

| | Congress passes the Gold Standard Act. People can officially exchange \$1 for 1/20.67 of an ounce of gold. | | |

6 ANALYZING CHANGE In your opinion, what was the most important change to banking? Why was this change so significant?

_____

_____

_____

_____

7 ANALYZING ISSUES One of the Fed's jobs is to monitor electronic payments, which occur when money from one person's bank account is transferred to another person's bank account. However, bitcoin, one of the newest forms of currency, works differently. Bitcoins are transferred directly from one person to another without banks as intermediaries. All bitcoin users share a public record of transactions, but the Fed does not supervise bitcoin payments. Given the events that led up to the creation of the Fed, do you think that the growing popularity of bitcoins will increase or decrease economic stability? Why?

_____

_____

_____

_____

ESSENTIAL QUESTION

How did the creation of the Fed improve our banking system?

Overview of the Federal Reserve System

DIRECTIONS: Read the information about the Federal Reserve System. Then answer the questions that follow.

EXPLORE THE CONTEXT: The Federal Reserve System, more commonly known as "the Fed," was established in 1913. The Fed is the nation's central bank. The Federal Reserve website publishes information about the Fed and its operations. This excerpt comes from an article about the purpose of the Fed.

SECONDARY SOURCE: ARTICLE

" The Federal Reserve System is the central bank of the United States. It performs five general functions to promote the effective operation of the U.S. economy and, more generally, the public interest. The Federal Reserve

- **conducts the nation's monetary policy** to promote maximum employment, stable prices, and moderate long-term interest rates in the U.S. economy;

- **promotes the stability of the financial system** and seeks to minimize and contain systemic risks through active monitoring and engagement in the U.S. and abroad;

- **promotes the safety and soundness of individual financial institutions** and monitors their impact on the financial system as a whole;

- **fosters payment and settlement system safety and efficiency** through services to the banking industry and the U.S. government that facilitate U.S.-dollar transactions and payments; and

- **promotes consumer protection and community development** through consumer-focused supervision and examination, research and analysis of emerging consumer issues and trends, community economic development activities, and the administration of consumer laws and regulations.

The framers of the Federal Reserve Act purposely rejected the concept of a single central bank. Instead, they provided for a central banking "system" with three salient features: (1) a central governing Board, (2) a decentralized operating structure of 12 Reserve Banks, and (3) a combination of public and private characteristics. . . .

In establishing the Federal Reserve System, the United States was divided geographically into 12 Districts, each with a separately incorporated Reserve Bank. District boundaries were based on prevailing trade regions that existed in 1913 and related economic considerations, so they do not necessarily coincide with state lines.

As originally envisioned, each of the 12 Reserve Banks was intended to operate independently from the other Reserve Banks. Variation was expected in discount rates—the interest rate that commercial banks were charged for borrowing funds from a Reserve Bank. The setting of a separately determined discount rate appropriate to each District was considered the most important tool of monetary policy at that time. "

—"Overview of the Federal Reserve System," 2018

VOCABULARY

moderate: reasonable

systemic: widespread

facilitate: enable; make possible

salient: main; significant

prevailing: current; existing

coincide: match; correspond to

1 SUMMARIZING What is the overall goal or purpose of the Fed?

_____

_____

2 ANALYZING IDEAS Reread the five general functions of the Fed. In your opinion, is one of the functions more important than the others? If so, which one? Why? If not, why do you think that all five functions are equally important?

_____

_____

_____

_____

_____

3A CITING TEXT EVIDENCE How many District Reserve Banks are there? How were their locations determined?

_____

_____

3B UNDERSTANDING CONTEXT The text says that each Reserve Bank was "intended to operate independently from the other Reserve Banks." Why might independent operations of each Reserve Bank have been important in 1913?

_____

_____

_____

_____

3C ANALYZING CHANGE The country has changed immensely since 1913. Do you think that independent District Reserve Banks are still an important feature of the Federal Reserve System? Why or why not?

_____

_____

_____

_____

Banking Today

DIRECTIONS: Search for evidence in Chapter 10, Lesson 3, to help you answer the following questions.

ESSENTIAL QUESTION

How has technology affected the way we use money today?

As you gather evidence to answer the Essential Question, think about:

- how the fractional reserve system expands bank deposits.
- the various services offered by banks.
- the importance of saving and building credit.

1 **INFERRING** The text says that the interest rate a bank pays on deposits "must be very close to rates paid by competing financial institutions." Based on what you know about competition and markets, why is this true?

_____

_____

2 **CONSTRUCTING HYPOTHESES** Why do you think the Fed established a reserve requirement for banks?

_____

_____

_____

3 **DETERMINING CENTRAL IDEAS** How do banks make a profit?

_____

_____

_____

_____

4 **EVALUATING** Look at Figure 10.3 in your Student Edition text. Choose one unnecessary fee and explain how you could avoid paying it.

_____

_____

_____

_____

My Notes

_____

_____

_____

_____

_____

_____

5 **INTEGRATING INFORMATION** Fill in the table with the advantages and disadvantages of several common banking services.

Banking Service	Advantages	Disadvantages
Checking Account (DDA)		
Savings Account and Time Deposit		
Debit Card		
Credit Card		
Smart Card		

6 **ANALYZING CENTRAL IDEAS** What are some actions that you can take now to begin preparing for financial success in the future?

_____

_____

_____

_____

_____

Copyright © McGraw-Hill Education; TEXT: Public Papers of the Presidents of the United States: Barack Obama, 2009, Vol. 1. Washington D.C.: U.S. Government Printing Office, 2011.

ESSENTIAL QUESTION

How has technology affected the way we use money today?

Remarks on Signing the Credit Card Accountability, Responsibility, and Disclosure Act of 2009

DIRECTIONS: Read the excerpt from a speech by President Barack Obama. Then answer the questions that follow.

EXPLORE THE CONTEXT: Studies show that Americans owe approximately $905 billion in credit card debt. On May 22, 2009, President Obama signed the Credit Card Accountability, Responsibility, and Disclosure Act of 2009, often called the Credit CARD Act. Its goal was to increase transparency and help consumers use credit responsibly, while still allowing credit card companies to make a reasonable profit. This excerpt comes from the speech President Obama gave immediately prior to signing the Credit CARD Act.

PRIMARY SOURCE: SPEECH

" You know, most Americans use credit cards all the time. In the majority of cases, this is a convenience or a temporary, occasional crutch, a means to make life a little easier, to make the rare, large, or unexpected purchase that's paid off as quickly as possible.

We've also seen credit cards become for a minority of customers part of an uneasy, unstable dependence. Some end up in trouble because of reckless spending or wishful thinking. Some get in over their heads by not using their heads. And I want to be clear: We do not excuse or condone folks who've acted irresponsibly. We don't excuse irresponsibility.

But the reason this legislation is so important is because there are many others . . . who have relied on credit cards not because they were avoiding responsibilities, but precisely because they wanted to meet their responsibilities and got trapped.

These are hard-working people whose hours were cut, or the factory closed, who turned to a credit card to get through a rough month, which turned into 2 or 3 or 6 months without a job. These are parents who found, to their surprise, that their health insurance didn't cover a child's expensive procedure and had to pay the hospital bill, families who saw their mortgage payments jump and used the credit card more often to make up the difference.

These are borrowers who discovered that credit card debt is all too easily a one-way street: It's easy to get in, but almost impossible to get out. It's also, by the way, a lot of small-business owners who have helped to finance their dream through credit cards and suddenly, in this economic downturn, find themselves getting hammered.

Part of this is the broader economy, but part of it is the practices of credit card companies. Contracts are drafted not to inform, but to confuse. Mysterious fees appear on statements, payment deadlines shift, terms change, interest rates rise. And suddenly, a credit card becomes less of a lifeline and more of an anchor. "

—Barack Obama, "Remarks on Signing the Credit Card Accountability, Responsibility, and Disclosure Act of 2009," May 22, 2009

VOCABULARY

reckless: careless; irresponsible

condone: approve of; excuse

hammered: harmed; defeated

1 **DETERMINING MEANING** Based on the context in which it is used, what does President Obama mean by the word *crutch*?

_____

2 **ANALYZING TEXT STRUCTURE** In the second paragraph, President Obama says, "And I want to be clear: We do not excuse or condone folks who've acted irresponsibly. We don't excuse irresponsibility." Why do you think he includes this statement?

_____

_____

_____

_____

_____

3 CIVICS Based on President Obama's speech and information in the Explore the Context section, what types of reforms might be included in the Credit CARD Act?

_____

_____

_____

_____

_____

4 **ANALYZING IDEAS** In the last sentence, President Obama says, "And suddenly, a credit card becomes less of a lifeline and more of an anchor." What does he mean by this statement?

_____

_____

_____

_____

5 **EVALUATING EVIDENCE** In your opinion, does President Obama make a strong argument for passing the Credit CARD Act? Why or why not?

_____

_____

_____

_____

_____

_____

ESSENTIAL QUESTIONS

How has money evolved to meet the needs of people everywhere?

How did the creation of the Fed improve our banking system?

How has technology affected the way we use money today?

My Notes

① Think About It

Review the Supporting Questions that you developed at the beginning of the unit. Review the evidence that you gathered in Chapter 10. Were you able to answer each Supporting Question?

If there was not enough evidence to answer your Supporting Questions, what additional evidence do you think you need to consider?

② Organize Your Evidence

Complete the chart below to summarize what you have learned about money and banking.

Colonial Forms of Money	
Characteristics of Money	1. 2. 3. 4.
Functions of Money	1. 2. 3.
The Evolution of Banking: 1860-1971	
How Modern Banks Work	

③ Talk About It

Work in small groups. Talk with your group and compare and contrast the information you included in your chart. How have money and banking evolved over time? What are the characteristics and functions of money?

④ Write About It

Choose one of the topics from the chart. Write a paragraph that discusses the topic in more depth.

_____

_____

_____

_____

_____

_____

_____

_____

_____

⑤ Connect to the Essential Questions

Imagine that you are an anthropologist (a scientist who studies people and cultures), and you have been hired by the U.S. government to study the money and banking system used by the people on a newly discovered island. First, decide what kind of money and banking system the people on the island use. Be creative! For example, the people on the island could use any items as money. They could even have a completely digital system in which no paper currency or coins are used.

Next, write a visual essay that you can give to the U.S. government to share your findings. In your essay, include images that show the forms of money used by the people of the island. You may draw these images or find images online. Then explain how the forms of money used on the island do or do not fulfill the characteristics and functions of money.

Conclude your essay with a detailed explanation of the banking system on the island. Does the island have a central organization similar to the Fed? If so, how does this organization manage the money supply? If not, how does the lack of a central organization affect the economic stability of the banking system?

As you create your visual essay, be sure to keep the Essential Questions in mind: *How has money evolved to meet the needs of people everywhere? How did the creation of the Fed improve our banking system? How has technology affected the way we use money today?* After you finish, review your essay carefully, checking for proper grammar, spelling, and punctuation, as well as clear, concise writing.

MAKE CONNECTIONS Banks in the United States are highly regulated by the government. For example, government regulations require examiners to assess the safety and soundness of banks. In order to make these decisions, examiners study how well the bank is managed, the bank's overall financial health, the quality of loans made by the bank, and the bank's ability to manage risk. Other regulations protect consumers by requiring banks to provide clear information about the terms of accounts and loans.

Despite the wide range of banking regulations, many bank customers are unaware of the laws that protect them and their financial assets when they use banking services. Choose one regulation or law that affects banks. Research your chosen regulation. Then create a poster informing customers about the purpose of the regulation and how it affects them. If possible, get permission from the manager of a local bank and hang your poster in the bank's lobby so that customers who visit the bank can become more informed.

_____

_____

_____

_____

_____

_____

_____

_____

_____

_____

_____

_____

_____

Economic Performance

In this unit, you will learn how economic activity and economic performance are measured, as well as how unemployment, poverty, and changing population trends affect the economy. You will also study the business cycle and causes and consequences of economic instability. Read the Essential Questions for both chapters in this unit and think about how they will help you understand economic performance and economic instability.

TALK ABOUT IT

Select one Essential Question from each chapter in this unit and discuss it with a partner. What type of information would you need to know in order to answer it? For example, to understand how unemployment affects the economy, you must first know how unemployment is defined and measured.

DIRECTIONS: Write down two Supporting Questions for each chapter that will help you understand one or more of the Essential Questions in the chapter.

Chapter 12 Evaluating the Economy
ESSENTIAL QUESTION

• *How do we determine the economic and social well-being of the United States?*

MY RESEARCH QUESTIONS

Supporting Question 1:

_____

_____

Supporting Question 2:

_____

_____

Chapter 13 Economic Instability

ESSENTIAL QUESTION

- *What are the causes and consequences of instability in the economy?*

MY RESEARCH QUESTIONS

Supporting Question 1:

_____

_____

Supporting Question 2:

_____

_____

INDEPENDENT INQUIRY ACTIVITY

Chapter 13

For Chapter 13, your teacher may ask you to conduct a research project using the Research Questions you have developed above. For this independent inquiry project, you will follow these steps.

1. Research the answers to your Supporting Questions using online and library resources in addition to the Student Edition text. Analyze the primary and secondary sources you have located and take notes.
2. Select a method to report your findings, such as a research paper, an oral presentation, or a visual essay. Prepare your findings and submit them to your teacher or share them with your class.
3. To conclude, think of ways you could take action based on your findings. Choose one way to get involved.

GUIDED INQUIRY ACTIVITY

Chapter 12

This unit's guided inquiry activity focuses on Chapter 12 *Evaluating the Economy*. In the guided inquiry activity, you will follow the same process as the independent activity; however, primary sources and questions about these sources and the Student Edition text are provided to help guide you through the inquiry process.

Reread the Supporting Questions you developed for Chapter 12 as you prepare to search for evidence in the Student Edition text.

Measuring the Nation's Output and Income

DIRECTIONS: Search for evidence in Chapter 12, Lesson 1, to help you answer the following questions.

1 **DETERMINING CENTRAL IDEAS** What is gross domestic product (GDP) and how is it measured?

_____

_____

_____

_____

_____

2 **ANALYZING IDEAS** Decide if each transaction is included in GDP and explain why or why not. The first one has been done for you as an example.

Transaction	Included in GDP?	Why or why not?
A cell phone company buys a battery and uses it to produce a new cell phone.	No	The battery is an intermediate product because it is used to make a phone that will be included in GDP.
A mother pays a teenager to babysit her children after school.		
A girl buys a shirt at a used clothing store.		
A woman repairs a leaky faucet in her home.		
A family purchases a kitchen table at a furniture store.		
A college student earns extra cash by copying DVDs and selling them to other students.		

ESSENTIAL QUESTION

How do we determine the economic and social well-being of the United States?

As you gather evidence to answer the Essential Question, think about:

- how GDP is used to measure national output.
- the limitations of using GDP as a measure of national output.
- the various methods used to measure national income.
- how economic models are used to represent the relationships between GDP, GNP, and the various sectors of the macroeconomy.

My Notes

_____

_____

_____

_____

_____

_____

3 **ANALYZING ISSUES** Why would GDP be an inaccurate measure of economic performance if a base year was not used?

_____

_____

_____

4 **SUMMARIZING** GDP is a useful measure of economic performance, but it has some limitations. What does GDP not tell us?

_____

_____

_____

5 **CONTRASTING** A friend tells you that GDP and GNP are the same. How would you explain the difference to your friend?

_____

_____

_____

_____

6 **DESCRIBING** Choose one measure of national income and explain what it is and how it is calculated.

_____

_____

_____

7 **DRAWING CONCLUSIONS** Look at Figure 12.2 in your Student Edition text. It shows how the business, government, and consumer sectors interact in the circular flow of economic activity. Why are the three sectors interconnected?

_____

_____

_____

_____

_____

ESSENTIAL QUESTION

How do we determine the economic and social well-being of the United States?

VOCABULARY

cartogram: a map in which the size of objects shown corresponds to a selected statistic, such as population, GDP, GDP per capita, votes for a particular candidate, etc.

World Gross Domestic Product Per Capita Cartogram

DIRECTIONS: Look at the cartogram showing world GDP per capita. Then answer the questions that follow. Refer to the Reference Atlas section of the Student Edition to see a larger version of the cartogram.

EXPLORE THE CONTEXT: GDP per capita is the amount of money each person would receive if a country's GDP were distributed evenly. It is calculated by dividing the total GDP of a country by that country's population. GDP per capita is a good way of comparing the standard of living and prosperity of several countries because it accounts for variations in GDP due to population size. For example, imagine that two countries, Country A and Country B, both have a GDP of $5 trillion. It may initially seem like people in the two countries are equally wealthy. However, if Country A has a population of 100 million, then its GDP per capita is $50,000. On the other hand, if Country B has a population of 500 million, then its GDP per capita is $10,000. This is a significant difference and suggests that people in Country B probably have a lower standard of living. This cartogram shows world GDP per capita. Unlike a map that shows the political boundaries and land size of each country, the size of the countries is determined by their GDP per capita. For this reason, the map looks distorted when compared to a traditional map of the world.

PRIMARY SOURCE: MAP

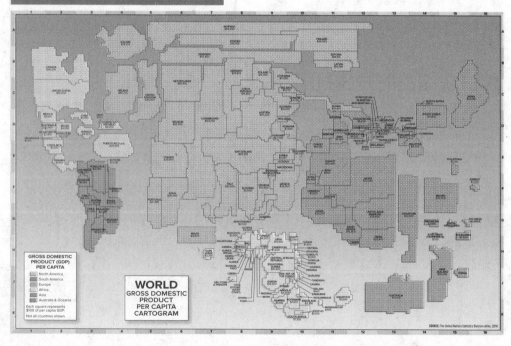

—The United Nations Statistics Division online, 2010

1A **DESCRIBING** What does each colored square on the cartogram represent?

_____

_____

_____

1B **INTERPRETING** Tonga is a small country near New Zealand. It is shown on the cartogram, but its GDP per capita is not labeled. What is its GDP per capita? How did you figure this out?

_____

_____

_____

2A **ANALYZING SOURCES** In which country is GDP per capita the highest? In which other countries is GDP per capita higher than average?

_____

_____

_____

2B GEOGRAPHY In which regions of the world is GDP per capita the lowest?

_____

_____

_____

3 **INFERRING** According to the cartogram, in 2010, the GDP per capita of the United States was $46,500, and the GDP per capita of Canada was $46,400. However, the GDP of the United States was about $15 trillion, while the GDP of Canada was about $1.6 trillion. What does this tell you about the population of the two countries?

_____

_____

_____

4 **PREDICTING** How do you think this cartogram might change in the future? Explain your reasoning. You may want to review Chapter 2 of your Student Edition text.

_____

_____

_____

Population Growth and Trends

DIRECTIONS: Search for evidence in Chapter 12, Lesson 2, to help you answer the following questions.

1 HISTORY What was the original purpose of the census? How is the census used today?

_____

_____

_____

_____

_____

_____

2 **ANALYZING CHANGE** How has the population of the United States changed since colonial times?

_____

_____

_____

_____

_____

3A **IDENTIFYING CAUSES** Why did many people move from rural areas to cities in the 1800s?

_____

_____

_____

3B **EXPLAINING CAUSE AND EFFECT** Why has the trend toward urbanization reversed in the past few decades? How has this affected regional migration patterns?

_____

_____

_____

_____

ESSENTIAL QUESTION

How do we determine the economic and social well-being of the United States?

As you gather evidence to answer the Essential Question, think about:

- how the population of the United States is counted.

- how the demographics of the United States have changed over time.

- the consequences of a growing, changing population.

- the challenges the United States might face in the future as a result of projected population changes.

My Notes

_____

_____

_____

_____

_____

_____

4 PREDICTING Based on the information in the "Consequences of Growth" section, how could city planners use knowledge of changing population trends to address potential problems before they arise?

_____

_____

_____

_____

5 EXPLAINING EFFECTS Why would the retirement of baby boomers place a large burden on younger workers?

_____

_____

_____

_____

6A SUMMARIZING For each factor affecting population growth, provide a definition and describe demographers' predictions.

Factors Affecting Population Growth	Definition	Predictions
Fertility Rate		
Life Expectancy		
Net Immigration		

6B INTEGRATING INFORMATION Based on information in the text and the chart in question 6A, how is the population of the United States expected to change in the future?

_____

_____

_____

ESSENTIAL QUESTION

How do we determine the economic and social well-being of the United States?

Congressional Reapportionment

DIRECTIONS: Look at the map showing congressional reapportionment. Then answer the questions that follow.

EXPLORE THE CONTEXT: The Constitution of the United States requires the government to take a census, or an official count of all the people living in the country. The first U.S. census was conducted in 1790, and a census has been conducted every ten years since then. One of the primary purposes of the census is to determine how many members of the House of Representatives each state will have for the next ten years. There are 435 representatives total, and the number each state gets is based on the state's population. All states get at least one representative, but states with larger populations get additional representatives. This map shows reapportionment that occurred due to population changes between 2000 and 2010.

PRIMARY SOURCE: MAP

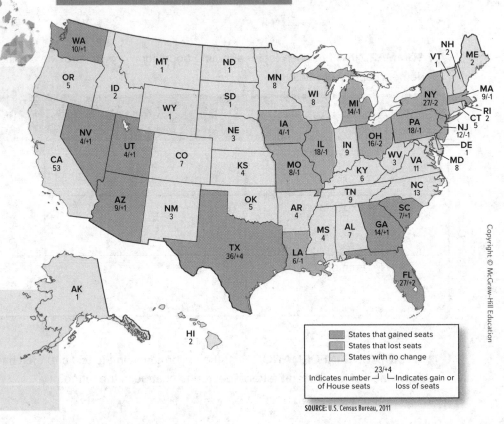

SOURCE: U.S. Census Bureau, 2011

VOCABULARY

reapportionment: redistribution; reallocation

① **USING MAPS** Which state has the largest population? How do you know?

_____

_____

2A GEOGRAPHY Which states gained representatives? Which states lost representatives? What does this tell you about the populations of these states?

_____

_____

_____

_____

2B **INTEGRATING INFORMATION** What are some possible reasons for these population gains and losses? You may want to review the information on population growth and regional change in Lesson 2 of your Student Edition text.

_____

_____

_____

3 **ANALYZING SOURCES** Is there a relationship between the physical size of a state (its land area) and the number of representatives it has? How do you know? Use a specific example to support your answer.

_____

_____

_____

_____

4 **PREDICTING** The next census will be in 2020. At that time, the number of representatives for each state may change again. Based on the projected changes discussed in your Student Edition text, what changes to apportionment might you expect as a result of the 2020 census?

_____

_____

_____

5 **ANALYZING ISSUES** While population determines how many representatives a state has, the number of senators each state has does not depend on the state's population. All states, regardless of population size, have two senators. Is this fair? Why or why not?

_____

_____

_____

Poverty and the Distribution of Income

DIRECTIONS: Search for evidence in Chapter 12, Lesson 3, to help you answer the following questions.

1 **SUMMARIZING** How were the poverty thresholds developed?

_____

_____

_____

_____

_____

_____

2 **CONSTRUCTING HYPOTHESES** The text says that children under 18 are the most vulnerable to poverty. Why do you think this is?

_____

_____

_____

_____

3 **INTERPRETING CHARTS/GRAPHS** How does the Lorenz curve show that income inequality increased between 1970 and 2012?

_____

_____

_____

4 **ANALYZING ISSUES** Differences in education contribute significantly to income inequality, yet studies show that about 6-7 percent of people aged 16-24 are not enrolled in school and do not have a high school diploma. How could we use tax money to reduce high school dropout rates?

_____

_____

_____

_____

ESSENTIAL QUESTION

How do we determine the economic and social well-being of the United States?

As you gather evidence to answer the Essential Question, think about:

- how poverty is defined.
- how income is distributed in the United States.
- why the distribution of income is unequal.
- whether antipoverty programs have been successful in the past.
- whether proposed antipoverty programs have the potential to be effective in the future.

My Notes

_____

_____

_____

_____

_____

5 **IDENTIFYING CAUSES** Review the nine reasons that incomes vary. Choose one and explain how it contributes to income inequality.

_____

_____

_____

6A **ANALYZING CENTRAL IDEAS** Fill in the table with information about each antipoverty program.

Antipoverty Program	How It Reduces Poverty
Temporary Assistance for Needy Families (TANF)	
Supplemental Security Income (SSI)	
Supplemental Nutrition Assistance Program (SNAP)	
Medicaid	
Social Service Programs	
Earned Income Tax Credit (EITC)	
Enterprise Zones	
Workfare	
Negative Income Tax	

6B **EVALUATING** In your opinion, which of the programs in question 6A would most effectively reduce poverty? Why?

_____

_____

_____

ESSENTIAL QUESTION

How do we determine the economic and social well-being of the United States?

Annual Message to the Congress on the State of the Union

DIRECTIONS: Read the excerpt from President Lyndon B. Johnson's 1964 State of the Union address. Then respond to the questions that follow.

EXPLORE THE CONTEXT: Lyndon B. Johnson became president after John F. Kennedy was assassinated in November 1963. President Johnson was known for his "War on Poverty," which ultimately led to the passage of several new laws intended to reduce poverty rates in the United States. This excerpt comes from his first State of the Union address, given on January 8, 1964, in which he first introduced the country to the War on Poverty.

PRIMARY SOURCE: SPEECH

66 This administration today, here and now, declares unconditional war on poverty in America. I urge this Congress and all Americans to join with me in that effort. It will not be a short or easy struggle, no single weapon or strategy will suffice, but we shall not rest until that war is won. The richest Nation on earth can afford to win it. We cannot afford to lose it. One thousand dollars invested in salvaging an unemployable youth today can return $40,000 or more in his lifetime.

Poverty is a national problem, requiring improved national organization and support. But this attack, to be effective, must also be organized at the State and the local level and must be supported and directed by State and local efforts. For the war against poverty will not be won here in Washington. It must be won in the field, in every private home, in every public office, from the courthouse to the White House. . . .

Very often a lack of jobs and money is not the cause of poverty, but the symptom. The cause may lie deeper in our failure to give our fellow citizens a fair chance to develop their own capacities, in a lack of education and training, in a lack of medical care and housing, in a lack of decent communities in which to live and bring up their children. . . .

Our aim is not only to relieve the symptom of poverty, but to cure it and, above all, to prevent it. No single piece of legislation, however, is going to suffice. We will launch a special effort in the chronically distressed areas of Appalachia. We must expand our small but our successful area redevelopment program. We must enact youth employment legislation to put jobless, aimless, hopeless youngsters to work on useful projects. We must distribute more food to the needy through a broader food stamp program. We must create a National Service Corps to help the economically handicapped of our own country as the Peace Corps now helps those abroad. We must modernize our unemployment insurance and establish a high-level commission on automation. If we have the brain power to invent these machines, we have the brain power to make certain that they are a boon and not a bane to humanity. 99

— Lyndon B. Johnson, "Annual Message to the Congress on the State of the Union," January 8, 1964

VOCABULARY

unconditional: total; absolute

suffice: be enough

salvaging: saving; rescuing

chronically: regularly; persistently

distressed: troubled

enact: pass; create

boon: benefit

bane: a cause of harm

1 **ANALYZING TEXT STRUCTURE** In the first paragraph, President Johnson compares the War on Poverty to a more traditional war. He does this by referring to weapons and strategies and discussing the War on Poverty as something that is won or lost. Do you think this comparison is effective? Does it increase the power of President Johnson's words? Why or why not?

_____

_____

_____

2 **IDENTIFYING CAUSES** According to President Johnson, what are the causes of poverty?

_____

_____

3 **DETERMINING CENTRAL IDEAS** What solutions or strategies does President Johnson hope to implement in order to help people who are living in poverty?

_____

_____

_____

_____

_____

4 **DETERMINING MEANING** President Johnson says, "Very often a lack of jobs and money is not the cause of poverty, but the symptom." What does he mean by this?

_____

_____

_____

5 **CONSTRUCTING HYPOTHESES** Before President Johnson's War on Poverty, the poverty rate in the United States was about 22 percent. Since the War on Poverty began, the poverty rate has remained steady at around 12-13 percent. Why do you think the poverty rate has remained steady? What could we do to lower the poverty rate further?

_____

_____

_____

_____

_____

ESSENTIAL QUESTION

How do we determine the economic and social well-being of the United States?

My Notes

_____

_____

_____

_____

_____

_____

_____

_____

_____

_____

_____

_____

① Think About It

Review the Supporting Questions that you developed at the beginning of the unit. Review the evidence that you gathered in Chapter 12. Were you able to answer each Supporting Question?

If there was not enough evidence to answer your Supporting Questions, what additional evidence do you think you need to consider?

_____

_____

_____

② Organize Your Evidence

Complete the chart below to explain how each factor affects economic and/or social well-being.

Factor	How This Factor Affects Economic and/or Social Well-Being
National Output (GDP)	
National Income (GNP, NNP, NI, PI, DPI)	
Population Growth and Regional Change	
Population Trends (age, gender, race, ethnicity, fertility, life expectancy, immigration, etc.)	
Poverty Rate and the Distribution of Income	

③ Talk About It

Work in small groups. Talk with your group and compare and contrast the information you included in your chart. How are economic and social well-being measured? How do economists use this information to evaluate the economy? How does the government use this information to improve economic and social well-being?

④ Write About It

Choose one of the topics from the chart. Write a paragraph that discusses the topic in more depth. Include specific details in your paragraph.

_____

_____

_____

_____

_____

_____

_____

⑤ Connect to the Essential Question

For this activity, you will be analyzing U.S. Census Bureau data related to population, race, income, education, age, or other factors. Then you will create a presentation comparing and analyzing data for two different years.

Navigate to the Population Estimates Edition of the Census Explorer at www.census.gov/censusexplorer/censusexplorer-popest.html or the People, Education, and Income Edition of the Census Explorer at www.census.gov/censusexplorer/censusexplorer.html.

Use the drop-down menu to select a measure, such as total population, median household income, or a specific education level. You may want to look at several measures before choosing the data set you want to focus on. When you have made a decision, sort the data by county. Then zoom in on the counties in a state of your choice.

Focus on two different years for which data are available. Use the tools on the website to create a map for each year. Analyze the data, paying special attention to differences between the two years. In which counties has the data stayed the same? In which counties have changes occurred? It may help to take screenshots of the data for each year and print them out or save them to your computer so you can view them side by side.

Once you have analyzed the data, create a presentation in which you share the changes that have occurred over time, present at least one theory explaining these changes, and discuss the future implications of your findings. You may need to do additional research in order to develop your theory and determine potential implications for the future. Rehearse your presentation and then share your findings with your class.

TAKE ACTION

MAKE CONNECTIONS Each year, the president gives a televised speech to a joint session of Congress. Except in the first year of a new president's term, this speech is called the State of the Union, and it is mandated by the U.S. Constitution. In a State of the Union address, the president talks about what has been accomplished in the last year and shares goals for the upcoming year. The speech usually addresses economic goals and any other important legislation or events.

Think about your school or school district. Then use the Department of Education website to research any economic and population-related trends and changes over the past few years. You may want to find answers to some or all of the following questions:

- What is the school or district's total budget?

- What are the school or district's largest sources of revenue?

- How much does the school or district spend on each student?

- How does the school or district allocate financial resources?

- What are the demographics of the school or district's teachers? The students? Consider gender, race, first language, and other characteristics.

- How many students transfer into the school or district each year? How many leave?

- How well do students perform on standardized tests?

- How many students qualify for a free or reduced-price lunch?

Once you have completed your research, write a "State of the School" or "State of the District" speech. Include your findings in your speech, as well as goals for the upcoming year. Rehearse your speech and present it to another class. You may also want to submit a written copy to the principal or the school board. If you receive a response, share it with your teacher and your class.

Government and the Economy

In this unit, you will learn how the government collects and spends money. Then you will study fiscal and monetary policy to see how the government promotes economic growth and stability. Read the Essential Questions for each of the three chapters in this unit and think about how they will help you understand government influence on the economy.

TALK ABOUT IT

Select one Essential Question from each chapter in this unit and discuss it with a partner. What type of information would you need to know in order to answer it? For example, to understand how monetary policy works, you first need to know why the Fed was created and how it is structured.

DIRECTIONS: Write down two Supporting Questions for each chapter that will help you understand one or more of the Essential Questions in the chapter.

Chapter 14 Taxes and Government Spending
ESSENTIAL QUESTION

- *How does the government collect revenue, and on what is that revenue spent?*

MY RESEARCH QUESTIONS

Supporting Question 1:

_____

_____

Supporting Question 2:

_____

_____

Chapter 15 Fiscal Policy
ESSENTIAL QUESTIONS

- *How does the government promote the economic goals of price stability, full employment, and economic growth?*

- *How do we know if macroeconomic equilibrium has been achieved?*

MY RESEARCH QUESTIONS

Supporting Question 1:

_____

_____

Supporting Question 2:

_____

_____

Chapter 16 Monetary Policy
ESSENTIAL QUESTION

- *How does the government promote the economic goals of price stability, full employment, and economic growth?*

MY RESEARCH QUESTIONS

Supporting Question 1:

_____

_____

Supporting Question 2:

_____

_____

INDEPENDENT INQUIRY ACTIVITIES

Chapters 15 and 16

For Chapters 15 and 16, your teacher may ask you to conduct a research project using the Research Questions you have developed above. For these independent inquiry projects, you will follow these steps.

1. Research the answers to your Supporting Questions using online and library resources in addition to the Student Edition text. Analyze the primary and secondary sources you have located and take notes.
2. Select a method to report your findings, such as a research paper, an oral presentation, or a visual essay. Prepare your findings and submit them to your teacher or share them with your class.
3. To conclude, think of ways you could take action based on your findings. Choose one way to get involved.

GUIDED INQUIRY ACTIVITY

Chapter 14

This unit's guided inquiry activity focuses on Chapter 14 *Taxes and Government Spending*. In the guided inquiry activity, you will follow the same process as the independent activities; however, primary sources and questions about these sources and the Student Edition text are provided to help guide you through the inquiry process.

Reread the Supporting Questions you developed for Chapter 14 as you prepare to search for evidence in the Student Edition text.

Taxes

DIRECTIONS: Search for evidence in Chapter 14, Lesson 1, to help you answer the following questions.

1 **SUMMARIZING** What are four ways that taxes impact the economy?

_____

_____

_____

_____

_____

_____

_____

2 **DRAWING CONCLUSIONS** The government decides to increase revenue by taxing the production of cigarettes. Can cigarette producers shift the incidence of the tax to consumers? Why or why not?

_____

_____

_____

_____

_____

3 **COMPARING** How do proportional, progressive, and regressive taxes differ?

_____

_____

_____

_____

_____

ESSENTIAL QUESTION

How does the government collect revenue, and on what is that revenue spent?

As you gather evidence to answer the Essential Question, think about:

- how taxes affect both businesses and consumers.
- what makes taxes effective.
- the various types of taxes, including possible alternatives to the current tax system.
- how taxes have changed since 1981.

My Notes

_____

_____

_____

_____

_____

_____

4 **ANALYZING IDEAS** The three criteria for effective taxes are equity, simplicity, and efficiency. Fill in the chart to decide if each type of tax meets the three criteria. Be sure to provide reasoning for your decisions.

Tax	Is it equitable? Why or why not?	Is it simple? Why or why not?	Is it efficient? Why or why not?
Sales Tax			
Individual Income Tax			
Medicare Tax			
Tolls			

5 **EVALUATING** Which alternative tax method do you think would work better in the United States: the flat tax or the value-added tax? Why?

_____

_____

_____

_____

ESSENTIAL QUESTION

How does the government collect revenue, and on what is that revenue spent?

The Progressive Caucus

DIRECTIONS: Read the speech from House of Representatives member Jared Polis. Then answer the questions that follow.

EXPLORE THE CONTEXT: In the United States, April 15 is known as Tax Day because it is the day when taxes are due to the federal government. On Tax Day, members of Congress often discuss current taxation policies. In 2010, Jared Polis, a representative for the state of Colorado, spoke about the importance of taxes.

PRIMARY SOURCE: CONGRESSIONAL RECORD

“ And this being tax time, everybody is reminded of how much they have to pay. And I think it's also important for us to remind them how much they get, the fact that people all over the world would risk dying, going across the desert to try to live in our country, what America stands for, globally, in terms of freedom, of unprecedented levels of prosperity that our middle-class families enjoy. That's what the American Dream is all about. That's what our country is all about. . . .

And even though I opposed the Iraq war and didn't like to see my tax dollars go there, even though I continue to oppose the escalation of troops in Afghanistan, and don't want to see my tax dollars going there, I know that the investment I make in paying my taxes is one that I can be proud of as an American. Knowing that it goes through title I to serve schools across our country that serve at-risk youth; knowing that it goes to help make health care more affordable for American families; knowing that it goes to help so that people who are unemployed don't lose their homes, can still put food on the table for their families; to know that our seniors have health care; to know that our young people have health care, and we're making it more accessible for people in the middle; to know that we're funding our roads, our bridges, our infrastructure, our arteries of commerce that empower the private sector to produce the prosperity that has made America unique—that's what it means to pay taxes.

That's why every year, in April, when I pay mine, I feel that same lump in my throat and in my belly as every American; but I know, deep inside, that I would not trade it for anything else. And I am proud that I have this opportunity to be able to contribute to this greatest of the great countries and help America continue to be a beacon unto the nations and a light for future generations. ”

—"The Progressive Caucus," Congressional Record, House of Representatives, April 15, 2010

VOCABULARY

unprecedented: never before seen; unmatched; unparalleled

escalation: increase

commerce: business; trade

beacon: inspiration; example

Copyright © McGraw-Hill Education; TEXT: U.S. Congress. House. The Progressive Caucus. Congressional Record: Proceedings and Debates of the 111th Congress, 2d sess. H. Rept. Vol. 156. By Keith Ellison. 111th Cong., 2d sess. H. Rept. Vol. 156. Washington D.C.; U.S. Government Printing Office, 2010. H2623.

1 **ANALYZING TEXT STRUCTURE** What is the purpose of the first paragraph of Polis's speech?

_____

_____

_____

2 **DETERMINING CENTRAL IDEAS** What types of expenditures is Polis proud to pay for with his tax dollars?

_____

_____

3 **DETERMINING MEANING** Polis says, "That's why every year, in April, when I pay mine, I feel that same lump in my throat and in my belly as every American; but I know, deep inside, that I would not trade it for anything else." What does Polis mean by this statement?

_____

_____

_____

_____

4 **ANALYZING POINT OF VIEW** In science, an artery carries blood from the heart to other organs. Based on the context in which it is used and the scientific meaning of the word _artery_, what does Polis mean by "arteries of commerce"? How does the use of the word _arteries_ contribute to the power of Polis's rhetoric?

_____

_____

_____

_____

5 **EVALUATING EVIDENCE** Do you agree with Polis that taxes are a small price to pay for the benefits of living in America, or do you think Polis is overlooking important negative aspects of taxes? Explain your reasoning.

_____

_____

_____

_____

Federal Government Finances

DIRECTIONS: Search for evidence in Chapter 14, Lesson 2, to help you answer the following questions.

1 SUMMARIZING How is the federal budget determined?

_____

_____

_____

_____

_____

_____

_____

2 COMPARING What is the difference between a budget deficit and a budget surplus?

_____

_____

_____

3 DETERMINING CENTRAL IDEAS What are the federal government's four largest sources of revenue? What are some other sources of revenue?

_____

_____

_____

_____

_____

4 ANALYZING CENTRAL IDEAS Why does Congress need approval for national defense expenditures? Why does Congress NOT need approval for Social Security expenditures?

_____

_____

_____

_____

ESSENTIAL QUESTION

How does the government collect revenue, and on what is that revenue spent?

As you gather evidence to answer the Essential Question, think about:

- how the annual federal budget is created.
- the federal government's sources of revenue.
- the federal government's expenditures.
- how deficit spending contributes to the national debt.
- how the national debt affects the economy.
- why it is difficult to reduce the national debt.

My Notes

_____

_____

_____

_____

_____

5 **ANALYZING IDEAS** How does the government fund deficit spending?

_____

_____

6 **IDENTIFYING EFFECTS** How does the national debt impact the economy?

_____

_____

7 HISTORY Fill in the chart with a description of each historical attempt to reduce the national debt. Then explain why each one failed. The first one has been done for you as an example.

Attempt	Description	Reason for Failure
Balanced Budget and Emergency Deficit Control Act of 1985	Mandated a balanced budget	Congress avoided the balanced budget law by passing spending bills that did not take effect for a few years. In 1990, the economy began to weaken, triggering a suspension of budget cuts.
Budget Enforcement Act of 1990		
Omnibus Budget Reconciliation Act of 1993		
Line-item veto		
Balanced Budget Agreement of 1997		
2011 sequester agreement between President Obama and Congress		

Statement on the Budget Surplus

ESSENTIAL QUESTION

How does the government collect revenue, and on what is that revenue spent?

DIRECTIONS: Read President Bill Clinton's statement on the budget surplus. Then answer the questions that follow.

EXPLORE THE CONTEXT: From 1998 to 2001, the federal government had a budget surplus. On May 21, 1999, President Clinton spoke about the surplus. He explained how it was affecting the economy and outlined his goals for the future. As you read, remember that the national debt is NOT the same as the national deficit or surplus. The national debt is the total amount owed, while the national deficit or surplus is the difference between revenue and expenditures.

PRIMARY SOURCE: SPEECH

66 Today I am pleased to announce that we are on track to reach the largest annual budget surplus ever. Thanks to solid fiscal discipline, the surplus at this point in the fiscal year is $64.7 billion, the largest in history over a comparable period.

When I came into office just over 6 years ago, we faced a deficit that had already risen to a staggering $290 billion and was projected to be over $400 billion in this fiscal year. The Vice President and I, working with Congress, set this country on a new course of fiscal discipline, enacting two strong budget packages in 1993 and 1997. As a result, we have begun to pay down the Nation's debt. In this quarter alone, we expect to pay down $116 billion of privately held marketable Federal debt, the largest sum ever in a single quarter.

Reducing the debt lowers long-term interest rates for home mortgages and autos and lowers borrowing costs for businesses, fueling private sector investments for continued economic growth. Despite the good news, this is not a time for complacency. We must renew our commitment to this sound economic strategy by making responsible investments in our people, working for open markets, and maintaining the fiscal discipline that is beginning to lift the crushing burden of debt from our children and grandchildren. It is especially critical that we create a bipartisan consensus for saving the surplus and paying down our national debt in a way that strengthens the solvency of both Social Security and Medicare. 99

—President Bill Clinton, "Statement on the Budget Surplus," May 21, 1999

VOCABULARY

projected: estimated; expected

enacting: passing

complacency: feeling secure; feeling like nothing needs to be done or changed

bipartisan: not affiliated with a particular political party

solvency: soundness; financial condition

1 **DETERMINING MEANING** What do you think President Clinton means by the term *fiscal discipline*?

_____

_____

2A **CITING TEXT EVIDENCE** What was the deficit when President Clinton took office in 1993? What was the projected deficit for 1999?

_____

_____

2B **INFERRING** Assuming that the deficit did not change significantly between May 21 and the end of the fiscal year, did the actual deficit for 1999 match the projected deficit for 1999? How do you know?

_____

_____

_____

3 **IDENTIFYING EFFECTS** According to President Clinton, how does reducing the debt affect the economy?

_____

_____

_____

4 **DETERMINING CENTRAL IDEAS** How does President Clinton hope to continue reducing the national debt in the future?

_____

_____

_____

_____

5 **ANALYZING POINT OF VIEW** In 1781, Alexander Hamilton wrote, "A national debt, if it is not excessive, will be to us a national blessing." Why would Hamilton consider a national debt to be a blessing? How might President Clinton respond to Hamilton's statement?

_____

_____

_____

_____

_____

_____

ESSENTIAL QUESTION

How does the government collect revenue, and on what is that revenue spent?

As you gather evidence to answer the Essential Question, think about:

- the various sources of state and local government revenue.
- state and local government expenditures.

State and Local Government Finances

DIRECTIONS: Search for evidence in Chapter 14, Lesson 3, to help you answer the following questions.

1 **DETERMINING CENTRAL IDEAS** What is intergovernmental revenue?

_____

_____

_____

_____

2 **COMPARING** How does the process of creating a state budget compare to the process of creating the federal budget?

_____

_____

_____

_____

_____

3 **SUMMARIZING** Fill in the charts to show the four largest sources of revenue and the four largest expenditures for state and local governments.

My Notes

_____

_____

_____

_____

_____

_____

Rank	State Governments	Local Governments
#1 Revenue Source		
#2 Revenue Source		
#3 Revenue Source		
#4 Revenue Source		

Rank	State Governments	Local Governments
#1 Expenditure		
#2 Expenditure		
#3 Expenditure		
#4 Expenditure		

4 **DIFFERENTIATING** Both state and local governments spend a lot of money on education. How do the recipients of these funds differ? Why might this be the case?

_____

_____

_____

_____

_____

5 **ANALYZING ISSUES** Some people feel that elementary and secondary schools should be funded by state governments or the federal government rather than by local governments. They believe that the current system is unfair because schools in wealthier areas, where property taxes are higher, have more funding than schools in less well-to-do regions. Others argue that the current system is fair because the children of people who pay higher property taxes also reap the benefits. Do you think the current system is fair? Why or why not?

_____

_____

_____

_____

_____

ESSENTIAL QUESTION

How does the government collect revenue, and on what is that revenue spent?

State Government Revenues and Expenditures and Local Government Revenues and Expenditures

DIRECTIONS: Study the graphs showing state and local government revenues and expenditures. Then answer the questions that follow.

EXPLORE THE CONTEXT: Both state and local governments have many sources of revenue and many expenditures. The top graph shows the typical revenue sources and expenditures for state governments. The bottom graph shows the typical revenue sources and expenditures for local governments.

SECONDARY SOURCE: GRAPH

Revenues = Expenditures plus Surplus

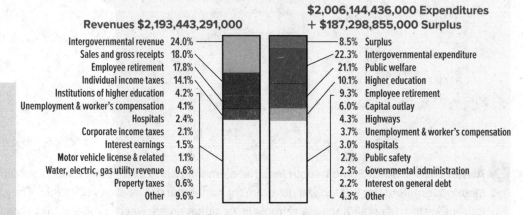

Revenues $2,193,443,291,000

$2,006,144,436,000 Expenditures
+ $187,298,855,000 Surplus

Revenue Source	%		%	Expenditure
Intergovernmental revenue	24.0%		8.5%	Surplus
Sales and gross receipts	18.0%		22.3%	Intergovernmental expenditure
Employee retirement	17.8%		21.1%	Public welfare
Individual income taxes	14.1%		10.1%	Higher education
Institutions of higher education	4.2%		9.3%	Employee retirement
Unemployment & worker's compensation	4.1%		6.0%	Capital outlay
Hospitals	2.4%		4.3%	Highways
Corporate income taxes	2.1%		3.7%	Unemployment & worker's compensation
Interest earnings	1.5%		3.0%	Hospitals
Motor vehicle license & related	1.1%		2.7%	Public safety
Water, electric, gas utility revenue	0.6%		2.3%	Governmental administration
Property taxes	0.6%		2.2%	Interest on general debt
Other	9.6%		4.3%	Other

SOURCE: U.S. Census Bureau, 2016

VOCABULARY

sales and gross receipts: a general term for any revenue collected from sales tax, as well as other revenue sources; examples of other revenue sources include sales of excess property, fishing/hunting licenses, tolls, library fees, and city parking fees

capital outlay: money spent to buy, fix, or upgrade capital assets, such as machinery, land, or facilities

worker's compensation: payments made to workers who are injured or become ill as a result of their job

Revenue = Expenditures and Surplus

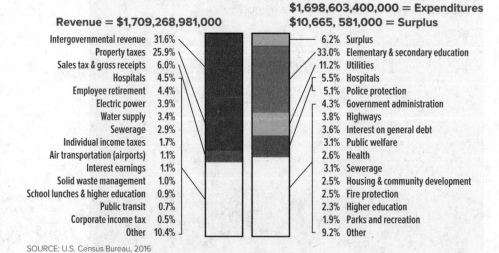

Revenue = $1,709,268,981,000

$1,698,603,400,000 = Expenditures
$10,665,581,000 = Surplus

Revenue Source	%		%	Expenditure
Intergovernmental revenue	31.6%		6.2%	Surplus
Property taxes	25.9%		33.0%	Elementary & secondary education
Sales tax & gross receipts	6.0%		11.2%	Utilities
Hospitals	4.5%		5.5%	Hospitals
Employee retirement	4.4%		5.1%	Police protection
Electric power	3.9%		4.3%	Government administration
Water supply	3.4%		3.8%	Highways
Sewerage	2.9%		3.6%	Interest on general debt
Individual income taxes	1.7%		3.1%	Public welfare
Air transportation (airports)	1.1%		2.6%	Health
Interest earnings	1.1%		3.1%	Sewerage
Solid waste management	1.0%		2.5%	Housing & community development
School lunches & higher education	0.9%		2.5%	Fire protection
Public transit	0.7%		2.3%	Higher education
Corporate income tax	0.5%		1.9%	Parks and recreation
Other	10.4%		9.2%	Other

SOURCE: U.S. Census Bureau, 2016

1A **INTERPRETING CHARTS/GRAPHS** What is the largest source of revenue for state governments? What is the largest expenditure for state governments?

_____

_____

1B **CIVICS** The United States uses a federal system, or a system in which power is divided between the federal government and state and local governments. Based on the federal structure of the United States, why does your answer to question 1A make sense?

_____

_____

_____

2 **COMPARING AND CONTRASTING** What is the same about state and local government revenue sources? What is different?

_____

_____

_____

_____

_____

3 **CONSTRUCTING HYPOTHESES** Many sources of revenue for state and local governments are also expenditures. Choose a revenue source that is also an expenditure. Explain why you think this revenue source would provide income while also requiring government spending.

_____

_____

_____

_____

4 **EVALUATING** What types of expenditures are unique to local governments? Is it fair that only local governments pay for these expenditures? Why or why not?

_____

_____

_____

_____

_____

_____

ESSENTIAL QUESTION

How does the government collect revenue, and on what is that revenue spent?

My Notes

① Think About It

Review the Supporting Questions that you developed at the beginning of the unit. Review the evidence that you gathered in Chapter 14. Were you able to answer each Supporting Question?

If there was not enough evidence to answer your Supporting Questions, what additional evidence do you think you need to consider?

② Organize Your Evidence

Complete the chart below to explain how governments collect and spend revenue.

Federal Government	Revenue Sources	Expenditures
State Government	Revenue Sources	Expenditures
Local Government	Revenue Sources	Expenditures

3 Talk About It

Work in small groups. Talk with your group and compare and contrast the information you included in your chart. How does each level of government collect revenue? How does each level of government spend money?

4 Write About It

Choose a level of government from the Organize Your Evidence chart. Write a paragraph that describes how that level of government earns revenue or spends money. Include specific details from your Student Edition text.

_____

_____

_____

_____

_____

_____

_____

_____

_____

_____

_____

_____

_____

5 Connect to the Essential Question

Research the budget for your town, focusing on the current year or a recent year. Find answers to the following questions: How does your town develop its annual budget? What are your town's main sources of revenue? How does your town allocate funds to pay for various expenditures? Is your town's budget balanced, or is your town running a deficit or a surplus?

Then write a newspaper article that could be published in the local paper. In your article, summarize your findings. Remember to define terms that may be unfamiliar to your readers. You should also include graphs and/or charts that enhance the reader's understanding of how the town earns or spends revenue. Revise your article, checking for proper grammar, spelling, and punctuation, as well as clear, concise writing. When you finish, send your article to the local paper for publication.

CITIZENSHIP
TAKE ACTION

MAKE CONNECTIONS Imagine that you are a member of the House of Representatives. You and your fellow House members have been asked to write a new tax law that will reduce the national debt.

There are four parts to this activity:

1. Research the current national debt, including current revenue and expenditures. Based on your findings, write a new tax law that will decrease the national debt. You may need to reduce spending, increase revenue, or combine both options to find the best solution. Remember that your tax law will need to gain the support of your fellow House members, as well as the Senate and the president, before it can be implemented, so be prepared to compromise.

2. Write a short speech that you can present to your fellow members of the House of Representatives. In your speech, provide a detailed description of your tax law and explain how your proposed law will reduce the national debt.

3. Rehearse your speech and present it to your classmates, who will represent other members of the House of Representatives. Listen to your classmates' speeches and evaluate their ideas.

4. As a class, vote on the best tax law proposal. Send the proposed tax law and a copy of the accompanying speech to your real House of Representatives member.

_____

_____

_____

_____

_____

_____

_____

_____

The Global Economy

In this unit, you will learn why countries trade and how foreign exchange works. Then you will study economic development around the globe, as well as how globalization and interdependence have changed the global economy. Finally, you will investigate ways to save and invest your own money. Read the Essential Questions for each of the three chapters in this unit and think about how they will help you understand the global economy and your own role within it.

TALK ABOUT IT

Select one Essential Question from each chapter in this unit and discuss it with a partner. What type of information would you need to know in order to answer it? For example, to understand why trade is beneficial, you must first understand absolute and comparative advantage.

DIRECTIONS: Write down two Supporting Questions for each chapter that will help you understand one or more of the Essential Questions in the chapter.

Chapter 17 Resources for Global Trade
ESSENTIAL QUESTION

•   *How does trade benefit all participating parties?*

MY RESEARCH QUESTIONS

Supporting Question 1:

_____

_____

Supporting Question 2:

_____

_____

Chapter 18 Global Economic Development
ESSENTIAL QUESTIONS

- *Why is the economic health of all nations important in a global economy?*

- *What are the challenges associated with globalization?*

MY RESEARCH QUESTIONS

Supporting Question 1:

_____

_____

Supporting Question 2:

_____

_____

Chapter 19 Personal Financial Literacy
ESSENTIAL QUESTIONS

- *How can financial institutions help you increase and better manage your money?*

- *What are the different types of business organizations?*

- *How can you take control of your own money?*

MY RESEARCH QUESTIONS

Supporting Question 1:

_____

_____

Supporting Question 2:

_____

_____

INDEPENDENT INQUIRY ACTIVITIES

Chapters 17 and 18

For Chapters 17 and 18, your teacher may ask you to conduct a research project using the Research Questions you have developed above. For these independent inquiry projects, you will follow these steps.

1. Research the answers to your Supporting Questions using online and library resources in addition to the Student Edition text. Analyze the primary and secondary sources you have located and take notes.
2. Select a method to report your findings, such as a research paper, an oral presentation, or a visual essay. Prepare your findings and submit them to your teacher or share them with your class.
3. To conclude, think of ways you could take action based on your findings. Choose one way to get involved.

GUIDED INQUIRY ACTIVITY

Chapter 19

This unit's guided inquiry activity focuses on Chapter 19 *Personal Financial Literacy*. In the guided inquiry activity, you will follow the same process as the independent activities; however, primary sources and questions about these sources and the Student Edition text are provided to help guide you through the inquiry process.

Reread the Supporting Questions you developed for Chapter 19 as you prepare to search for evidence in the Student Edition text.

Financial Institutions and Your Money

DIRECTIONS: Search for evidence in Chapter 19, Lesson 1, to help you answer the following questions.

Look at your sister's monthly budget. Then answer questions 1A and 1B.

Category	Amount Spent
Housing	
Rent	$1,000
Utilities (gas, water, electricity)	$150
Phone/Internet service	$80
Food	
Groceries	$100
Restaurants	$50
Transportation	
Gasoline	$80
Car Insurance	$300
Entertainment	
Books	$30
Movies	$20
Health Care	
Health Insurance	$90
TOTAL EXPENSES	**$1,900**

ESSENTIAL QUESTION

How can financial institutions help you increase and better manage your money?

As you gather evidence to answer the Essential Question, think about:

- how financial institutions can help you save your money.
- the wide range of services offered by financial institutions.
- ways to make yourself a creditworthy borrower.

My Notes

1A **INTERPRETING** Your sister earns $2,000 per month. Is your sister's budget effective? Why or why not?

_____

_____

_____

_____

_____

1B **ANALYZING ISSUES** Your sister's car has a flat tire. Replacing the tire will cost about $150. Suggest a way that your sister can reduce her expenses in order to have enough money to replace the tire.

_____

_____

_____

2 COMPARING Fill in the Venn diagram comparing commercial banks and credit unions.

```
     Commercial Banks          Both          Credit Unions
```

3 ANALYZING IDEAS A depositor has a choice between three savings accounts. The first account offers simple interest of 5 percent per year. The second account offers 5 percent interest that is compounded annually. The third account offers 5 percent interest that is compounded daily. If the accounts are identical in every other way, which account should the depositor choose? Why?

_____

_____

_____

4 ANALYZING CENTRAL IDEAS Your friend wants to open a savings account at a bank. She can only afford to make an initial deposit of $100, and she wants to earn as much interest as possible. However, she cannot afford to lose her money, so she wants an account with no risk. She will not need the money until she starts college in two years. What kind of account would you recommend for your friend? Why?

_____

_____

5 SUMMARIZING How can you build credit?

_____

_____

6 IDENTIFYING EFFECTS What happens if you do not pay back borrowed money?

_____

_____

_____

ESSENTIAL QUESTION

How can financial institutions help you increase and better manage your money?

VOCABULARY

credit limit: the maximum amount of money you can borrow

credit card balance: the amount of money you have charged; the amount of money you owe to the lender

dispute: challenge; call into question

How Do I Get and Keep a Good Credit Score?

DIRECTIONS: Read the information about credit scores. Then answer the questions that follow.

EXPLORE THE CONTEXT: The Consumer Financial Protection Bureau (CFPB) was created in 2011 in response to the lending abuses that significantly contributed to the Great Recession. The CFPB's main job is protecting consumers from unfair lending practices. The CFPB also provides financial information for consumers. This article is from the CFPB website. It discusses ways that consumers can build and maintain a good credit score.

SECONDARY SOURCE: GOVERNMENT WEBSITE

❝ There is no secret formula to building a strong credit score, but there are some guidelines that can help.

- **Pay your loans on time, every time.** One way to make sure your payments are on time is to set up automatic payments, or set up electronic reminders. If you've missed payments, get current and stay current.

- **Don't get close to your credit limit.** Credit scoring models look at how close you are to being "maxed out," so try to keep your balances low compared to your total credit limit. If you close some credit card accounts and put most or all of your credit card balances onto one card, it may hurt your credit score if this means that you are using a high percentage of your total credit limit. Experts advise keeping your use of credit at no more than 30 percent of your total credit limit. You don't need to revolve on credit cards to get a good score. Paying off the balance each month helps get you the best scores.

- **A long credit history will help your score.** Credit scores are based on experience over time. The more experience your credit report shows with paying your loans on time, the more information there is to determine whether you are a good credit recipient.

- **Only apply for credit that you need.** Credit scoring formulas look at your recent credit activity as a signal of your need for credit. If you apply for a lot of credit over a short period of time, it may appear to lenders that your economic circumstances have changed negatively.

- **Fact-check your credit reports.** If you spot suspected errors, dispute them. If you have old credit card accounts you are not using, keep an eye on them to make sure that an identity thief is not using them. ❞

—Consumer Financial Protection Bureau, "How Do I Get and Keep a Good Credit Score?"

1 DETERMINING MEANING Based on the context in which it is used, what does it mean if you are "maxed out"?

_____

2A DRAWING CONCLUSIONS Sally got her first credit card three months ago. Her credit limit is $2,000, and her minimum monthly payment is $25. In the first month, she spent $1,500 and made the minimum payment. In the second month, she spent $1,800 and made a $40 payment. In the third month, she spent $1,900 and made the minimum payment. Is Sally likely to have a good credit score? Why or why not?

_____

_____

_____

_____

2B ANALYZING IDEAS What advice would you give Sally to help her improve her credit score?

_____

_____

_____

_____

3 INFERRING The text says, "Experts advise keeping your use of credit at no more than 30 percent of your total credit limit." Why would credit bureaus award higher credit scores to people who use less than 30 percent of their available credit?

_____

_____

_____

4 CONSTRUCTING HYPOTHESES Studies show that older people tend to have higher credit scores than younger people. Based on the information in the article, what might account for this finding?

_____

_____

_____

_____

ESSENTIAL QUESTION

What are the different types of business organizations?

As you gather evidence to answer the Essential Question, think about:

- the advantages and disadvantages of sole proprietorships, partnerships, and corporations.
- how businesses raise capital.
- the risks and rewards of investing in stocks and bonds.
- the benefits of investing in an Individual Retirement Account (IRA).

My Notes

_____

_____

_____

_____

_____

_____

_____

Business Organizations and Your Money

DIRECTIONS: Search for evidence in Chapter 19, Lesson 2, to help you answer the following questions.

1 **SUMMARIZING** Fill in the chart with the definition, advantages, and disadvantages of each type of business organization.

Business Organization	Definition	Advantages	Disadvantages
Sole Proprietorship			
Partnership			
Corporation			

2 **COMPARING** How do sole proprietorships and partnerships obtain capital? How does this differ from the ways that corporations obtain capital?

_____

_____

_____

_____

3 **ANALYZING IDEAS** Your friend wants to invest in stocks, and he asks you how he can reduce the risk of losing his investment. What advice would you give him?

_____

_____

_____

_____

4 **DIFFERENTIATING** How do Treasury instruments, municipal bonds, and corporate bonds differ?

_____

_____

_____

_____

_____

5 **ANALYZING CENTRAL IDEAS** Why is an Individual Retirement Account (IRA) both an investment and a form of savings?

_____

_____

_____

6 **EVALUATING** Would you prefer to have a Traditional IRA or a Roth IRA? Why?

_____

_____

_____

_____

ESSENTIAL QUESTION

What are the different types of business organizations?

What Is Diversification?

DIRECTIONS: Read the article on portfolio diversification. Then answer the questions that follow.

EXPLORE THE CONTEXT: The Securities and Exchange Commission, commonly referred to as the SEC, is a U.S. government agency. It is responsible for protecting investors and ensuring that markets where securities are sold are fair and efficient. Securities are stocks, bonds, and other financial assets. This article comes from a website run by the SEC's Office of Investor Education and Advocacy. It discusses ways that investors can diversify their portfolios.

VOCABULARY

allocate: distribute; divide up

asset: a bond, stock, or other financial claim on a borrower

sector: segment; part

index fund: a type of mutual fund that invests in all the companies in a particular stock market index, such as the Standard & Poor's 500 or the Dow Jones Industrial Average; some index funds focus on a smaller group of highly successful companies, while other index funds, called total stock market index funds, allow investors to invest in most or all of the publicly traded stocks in the U.S. or another country

SECONDARY SOURCE: GOVERNMENT WEBSITE

“The practice of spreading money among different investments to reduce risk is known as diversification. Diversification is a strategy that can be neatly summed up as "Don't put all your eggs in one basket."

One way to diversify is to allocate your investments among different kinds of assets. Historically, stocks, bonds, and cash have not moved up and down at the same time. Factors that may cause one asset class to perform poorly may improve returns for another asset class. People invest in various asset classes in the hope that if one is losing money, the others make up for those losses.

You'll also be better diversified if you spread your investments within each asset class. That means holding a number of different stocks or bonds, and investing in different industry sectors, such as consumer goods, health care, and technology. That way, if one sector is doing poorly, you may offset it with other holdings in sectors that are doing well.

Some investors find it easier to diversify by owning mutual funds. A mutual fund is a company that pools money from many investors and invests the money in stocks, bonds, and other financial products. Mutual funds make it easy for investors to own a small portion of many investments. A total stock market index fund, for example, owns stock in thousands of companies, providing a lot of diversification for one investment.

A mutual fund won't necessarily provide diversification, especially if it focuses on only one industry sector. If you invest in narrowly focused mutual funds, you may need to invest in several to be diversified. As you add more investments to your portfolio, you'll likely pay additional fees and expenses, which will lower your investment returns. So you'll need to consider these costs when deciding the best way to diversify your portfolio.”

—U.S. Securities and Exchange Commission, "What Is Diversification?"

1 INFERRING Think about the meaning of the statement, "Don't put all your eggs in one basket." How does this statement relate to the concept of diversification?

_____

_____

_____

2A SUMMARIZING According to the article, how can investors ensure that their portfolio is diverse? How should they allocate their investments?

_____

_____

_____

2B EVALUATING An investor has $50,000. She plans to put $5,000 in a savings account and invest the rest in stocks issued by two technology companies. Is this a good investment plan? Why or why not?

_____

_____

_____

_____

2C ANALYZING INFORMATION Reread the investor's plan in question 2B. Provide a suggestion to help the investor increase the diversification of her portfolio.

_____

_____

_____

_____

3A DETERMINING CENTRAL IDEAS Why do mutual funds usually help investors diversify?

_____

_____

3B ANALYZING CENTRAL IDEAS Under what circumstances would investing in a mutual fund not provide diversification?

_____

_____

Personal Money Decisions

DIRECTIONS: Search for evidence in Chapter 19, Lesson 3, to help you answer the following questions.

1 **CITING TEXT EVIDENCE** What does FAFSA stand for? What is the purpose of the FAFSA form?

_____

_____

_____

2 **CONTRASTING** How are student loans different from scholarships and grants?

_____

_____

3 **SUMMARIZING** Outside of loans, grants, and scholarships, what are some other ways to pay for college?

_____

_____

_____

_____

_____

4 **DETERMINING CENTRAL IDEAS** What should you consider before renting an apartment?

_____

_____

_____

_____

_____

ESSENTIAL QUESTION

How can you take control of your own money?

As you gather evidence to answer the Essential Question, think about:

- the various ways to pay for college.
- the advantages and disadvantages of renting and buying a home.
- the types of insurance you may want to buy.
- the benefits of donating to charity.

My Notes

_____

_____

_____

_____

_____

5 **ANALYZING ISSUES** Fill in the chart to analyze the advantages and disadvantages of renting and buying a home.

	Advantages	Disadvantages
Renting		
Buying		

6 **INFERRING** Under what circumstances might it be beneficial to have an adjustable rate mortgage (ARM)?

_____

_____

_____

7 **ANALYZING CHANGE** What types of insurance would you want to have at this point in your life? Do you think you might need more types of insurance in 10 or 20 years? Why?

_____

_____

_____

_____

8 **EVALUATING** Choose a charitable organization or charitable cause that is important to you. Explain how you could contribute to this organization or cause.

_____

_____

_____

ESSENTIAL QUESTION

How can you take control of your own money?

Unemployment and Earnings

DIRECTIONS: Study the graph showing how educational attainment affects earnings and unemployment. Then answer the questions that follow.

EXPLORE THE CONTEXT: The Bureau of Labor Statistics (BLS) is part of the U.S. Department of Labor. The BLS collects and analyzes data related to employment, prices, consumer expenditures, wages, and other similar categories. This information is published and made available to the public. This graph was created using 2014 data on educational attainment, wages, and unemployment. In general, as you move from left to right on the graph, more years of schooling are required to obtain each degree. For example, an associate's degree usually requires two years of schooling after high school, while a professional degree may require seven to ten years of schooling after high school, plus additional years of on-the-job training.

VOCABULARY

occupational program: teaches workers the skills needed for a specific career, such as hairstylist, auto repair technician, or dental assistant; often viewed as an alternative to an associate's or bachelor's degree

associate's degree: mostly offered by community colleges; coursework focuses on general academic knowledge

bachelor's degree: usually includes general academic knowledge as well as more advanced coursework in a specific field

master's degree: applicants must already have a bachelor's degree; coursework focuses on specialized knowledge in a specific field

doctoral degree: applicants must already have a bachelor's degree; coursework focuses on research and in-depth knowledge of a specific subject

professional degree: applicants must already have a bachelor's degree; focuses on the highly-specialized skills needed for a particular career; examples include medical doctors and lawyers

SECONDARY SOURCE: GRAPH

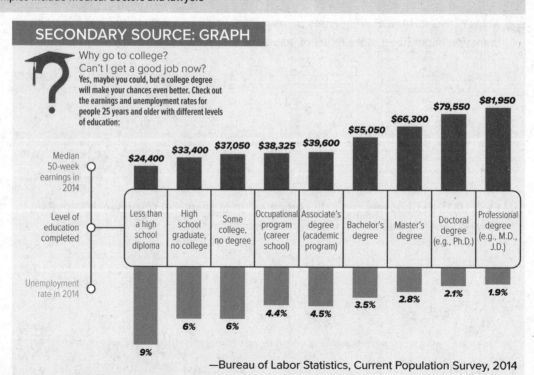

Why go to college? Can't I get a good job now? Yes, maybe you could, but a college degree will make your chances even better. Check out the earnings and unemployment rates for people 25 years and older with different levels of education:

—Bureau of Labor Statistics, Current Population Survey, 2014

1 **DESCRIBING** What is the relationship between education and earnings? Between education and unemployment?

_____

2A **INTERPRETING CHARTS/GRAPHS** Look at the salaries for each level of education. Between which two levels does the largest increase in salary occur?

_____

_____

2B **CONSTRUCTING HYPOTHESES** Review the vocabulary words and Explore the Context section. What factors might explain your answer to question 2A?

_____

_____

_____

_____

3 **COMPARING** At which three educational levels is salary almost the same?

_____

_____

_____

4 **ANALYZING ISSUES** Why would workers with a doctoral degree or a professional degree be the least likely to be unemployed and the most highly paid? Incorporate the concept of supply and demand into your answer.

_____

_____

_____

_____

_____

_____

5 **PREDICTING** In 1940, about 25 percent of adults had at least a high school diploma, while about 5 percent of adults had a bachelor's degree or higher degree. By 2015, 88 percent of adults had at least a high school diploma, while almost 33 percent of adults had a bachelor's degree or higher degree. If the number of high school and college graduates continues to increase steadily in the future, how might this affect the salary and unemployment rates shown on the graph?

_____

_____

_____

_____

ESSENTIAL QUESTIONS

How can financial institutions help you increase and better manage your money?

What are the different types of business organizations?

How can you take control of your own money?

My Notes

❶ Think About It

Review the Supporting Questions that you developed at the beginning of the unit. Review the evidence that you gathered in Chapter 19. Were you able to answer each Supporting Question?

If there was not enough evidence to answer your Supporting Questions, what additional evidence do you think you need to consider?

❷ Organize Your Evidence

Complete the chart to analyze how each account or investment helps your money grow, as well as the potential risks and rewards of each. The first one has been done for you as an example.

Account or Investment	How Your Money Grows	Risks and Rewards
Passbook Account	Passbook accounts earn interest at a fixed rate.	No risk; minimal reward.
Money Market Deposit Account		
Money Market Mutual Fund		
Certificate of Deposit (CD)		
Checking Account/ Demand Deposit Account (DDA)		
Stocks		
Bonds		
Individual Retirement Account (IRA)		

③ Talk About It

Work in small groups. Talk with your group and compare and contrast the information you included in your chart. How does each account or investment help your money grow? What is the relationship between risk and reward?

④ Write About It

Choose one of the topics from the chart. Write a paragraph that discusses the topic in more depth.

_____

_____

_____

_____

_____

_____

⑤ Connect to the Essential Questions

Imagine that you have just received a gift of $5,000. You plan to invest the money so that it grows and can be used for a down payment on a home in the future. Consider how you can best help your money grow. For example, should you put the money in a savings account? Should you buy stocks or bonds? Should you divide the money up and allocate some part of it to various investments? How can you maximize your rewards while minimizing the risk of losing your money?

Write a detailed investment plan that explains how you plan to invest the money and provides logical reasoning for your decisions. In addition to a written description, include at least one graph or chart that enhances the reader's understanding of your investment plan. When you finish, reread your work, revising for clarity and editing for proper grammar, spelling, and punctuation. Share your work with a partner and compare your investment plans.

TAKE ACTION

MAKE CONNECTIONS Giving to charity has many benefits, and you can contribute even if you cannot afford to donate money. Work with other students in your class to list as many charitable organizations as possible. Then choose the charity that most appeals to you. Go to the charity's website and research ways to volunteer your time or contribute in another manner. For example, you might choose to go through your closet and donate clothes you no longer wear to Goodwill. You might lead a pet food drive at your school and donate the food to an animal shelter. Or you could have a bake sale and donate the proceeds to the Red Cross.

Make time to contribute to your chosen charity in the next few weeks. Then create a final product that shows others how you contributed. Your final product could be a journal, a video diary, a scrapbook with photos and captions, a slide show, a short essay, a comic strip, or some other item. Share your product with other students in your class.